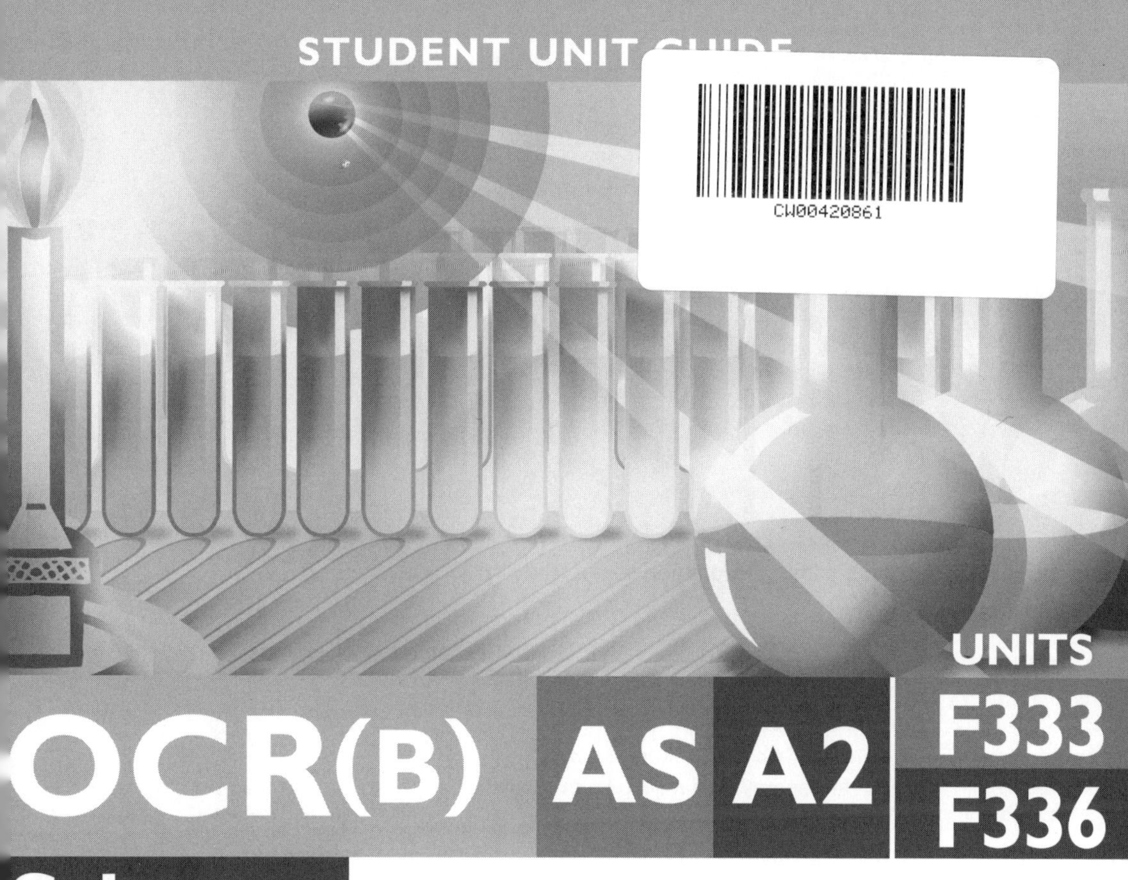

OCR(B) AS A2

UNITS F333 F336

Salters

Chemistry

Chemistry in Practice and Individual Investigation

Frank Harriss

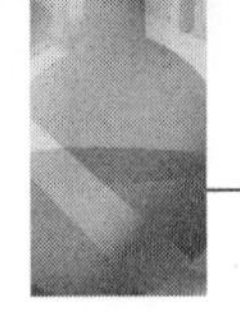

To Maggi

Philip Allan Updates, an imprint of Hodder Education, an Hachette UK company, Market Place, Deddington, Oxfordshire OX15 0SE

Orders
Bookpoint Ltd, 130 Milton Park, Abingdon, Oxfordshire OX14 4SB
tel: 01235 827720
fax: 01235 400454
e-mail: uk.orders@bookpoint.co.uk
Lines are open 9.00 a.m.–5.00 p.m., Monday to Saturday, with a 24-hour message answering service. You can also order through the Philip Allan Updates website: www.philipallan.co.uk

ISBN 978-1-4441-0845-3

First printed 2010
Impression number 5 4 3 2 1
Year 2014 2013 2012 2011 2010

This guide has been written specifically to support students preparing for the OCR (Salters) AS/A2 Chemistry Units F333 & F336 examinations. The content has been neither approved nor endorsed by OCR and remains the sole responsibility of the author.

Typeset by Pantek Arts Ltd, Maidstone, Kent.
Printed by MPG Books, Bodmin

Contents

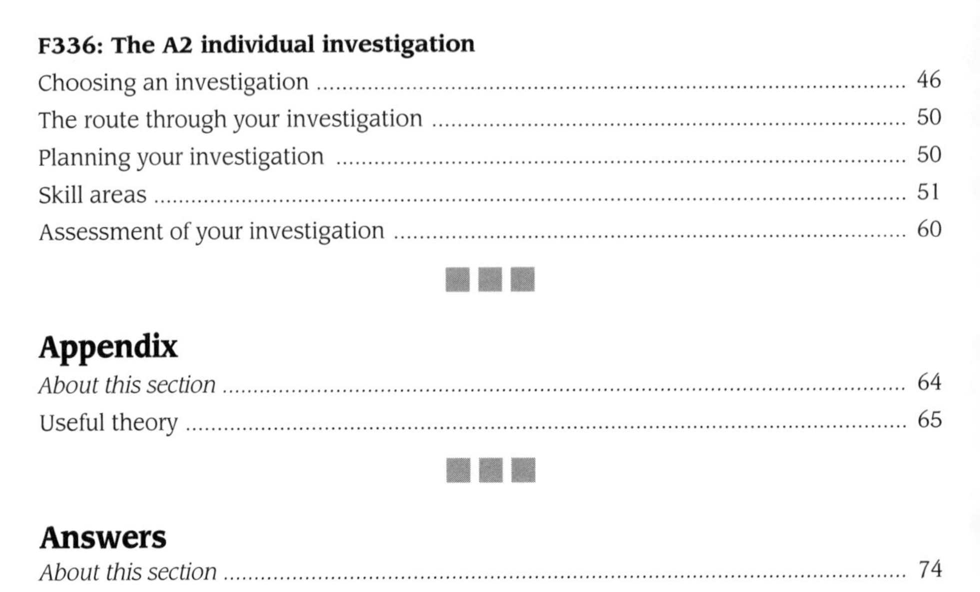

F336: The A2 individual investigation

Appendix

Answers

Introduction

About this guide

This guide is written for students studying the OCR (Salters) AS/A2 Chemistry course. It provides advice on the AS coursework unit **F333: Chemistry in Practice** and the A2 coursework unit **F336: Chemistry Individual Investigation**. The guide should be used in conjunction with the instructions you get from your teacher.

The guide is structured as follows:

- The first section gives general advice on matters to do with practical work.
- The second section gives advice for the AS coursework and the A2 individual investigation.
- The appendix contains some extra areas of chemistry theory that may be useful in investigations.
- Questions are given throughout to enable you to test your understanding. The answers are given at the back of the guide, but be sure you attempt the questions before looking at the answers.

Good luck with your AS tasks and your A2 individual investigation.

Safety

Some chemicals and apparatus are dangerous, yet accidents rarely occur in chemistry laboratories because teachers and students are careful to observe safety rules. You will have been given the rules for your school or college laboratory and you should follow them carefully.

Rules of admission to the laboratory

You will not be allowed into the laboratory unless a qualified adult is there to supervise you. Do not break this rule.

Protective clothing

- You must wear safety spectacles in the laboratory. Some experiments require goggles or a face shield.
- Laboratory coats should be worn, according to the instructions of your school or college.
- For some experiments, protective gloves should be worn.

Rules concerning chemicals

- Always follow instructions regarding chemicals, and use only those that are specified for a particular experiment.
- If you have an accident, inform a teacher at once — never try to conceal it.
- Do not take chemicals out of the laboratory.
- Smell chemicals only when instructed to do so and then waft the vapour towards your nose.
- Never eat or drink in the laboratory because your hands may be contaminated with chemicals.

Rules concerning apparatus

- Certain apparatus can be dangerous — for example, anything hot or broken glassware.
- Be careful when placing a rubber tube onto a glass tube (even fitting a pipette filler) — hold the two with your hands close together.
- If you have an accident, tell your teacher.

Following instructions

- In the laboratory, you must carry out only the experiments you have been told to do, not others that you have devised. If you feel that an 'extra' experiment would be a good idea, consult your teacher.
- Some experiments must be carried out in a fume cupboard.
- In your investigation, you will carry out several experiments that you have devised yourself. However, you must have given thought to these and written **risk assessments** (see p. 53) to which your teacher must agree before you start.

Behaviour

- If you are normally of a carefree disposition, save this for outside the laboratory — a few moments of carelessness could cause an accident.
- Follow rules about where you should leave bags, coats etc. when working in the laboratory.

Practical chemistry

The first part of this section deals with obtaining, recording and processing the results (both numerical results and descriptive observations) of practical chemistry experiments.

This material is important for all chemistry students. For students studying Salters A-level chemistry, it is equally relevant to the A2 investigation and the AS tasks.

The second part describes practical techniques. Some of these are relevant to AS. All are relevant to the A2 investigations, although you will only use a few of them in any one investigation.

Experimental results

Reading instruments

If you are carrying out a quantitative experiment, you will have to read measurements from instruments, such as burettes, measuring cylinders, thermometers, balances and timers.

Burettes and measuring cylinders

The technique here is to read the bottom of the meniscus — the curved surface that a liquid takes up in contact with glass (see Figure 1).

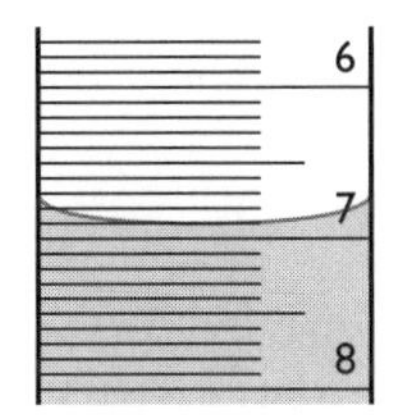

Figure 1 A burette reading 6.90 cm³

50 cm³ burettes are always read to the nearest 0.05 cm³, i.e. half the unit marked on the glassware.

Measuring cylinders come in different sizes but they should also be read to half the unit marked. For example, a 250 cm³ measuring cylinder is marked in 2 cm³ gradations, so it should be read to the nearest 1 cm³.

Questions

(1) Read the burettes shown in Figure 2.

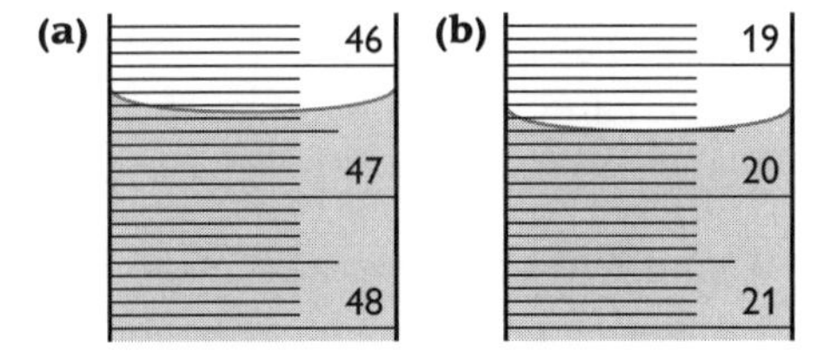

Figure 2 Read the burettes

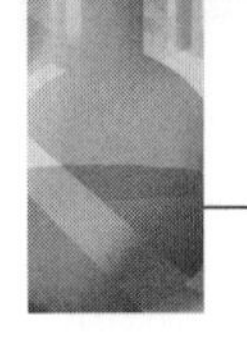

(2) Read the measuring cylinders shown in Figure 3, to the usual degree of precision.

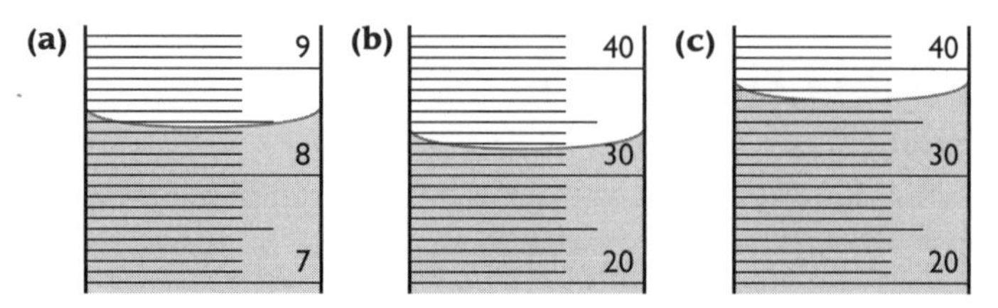

Figure 3 Read the measuring cylinders

Thermometers

These are read to half the smallest marked unit. Therefore, a thermometer marked in units of 1°C is read to the nearest 0.5°C and a thermometer marked in 0.1°C units is read to 0.05°C. For example, the temperature in Figure 4 would be recorded as 6.5°C.

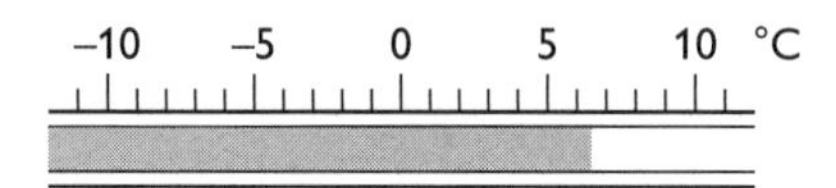

Figure 4 A thermometer reading 6.5°C

Question

(3) Read the thermometers shown in Figure 5.

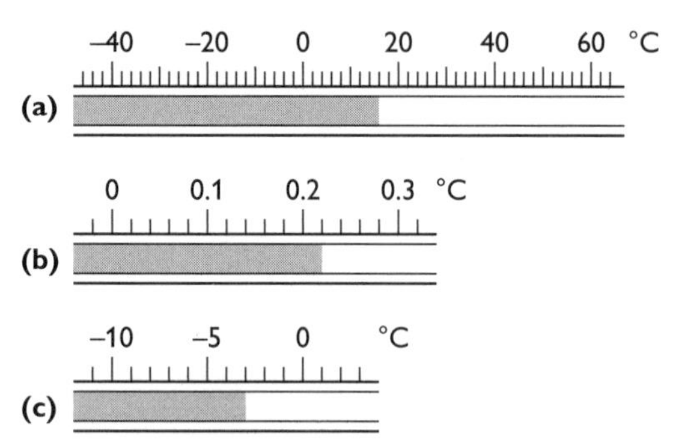

Figure 5 Read the thermometers

Digital instruments

These are read from the display. If the last place is flickering or moving from one figure to the next, you might decide to record to one less place.

Reading balances

The best way to weigh out a substance is to use a weighing bottle or 'weighing boat'. Weigh the boat plus contents beforehand, then tip out the contents and weigh the boat again. If any substance sticks to the boat, it will not introduce an error.

Where appropriate, a shortcut is to use the 'tare' control on the balance. Place the boat on the balance and press 'tare'. The reading will go to zero. Then add the substance to the boat and record the mass. This method is quicker and works well if you can be sure that all the substance leaves the boat when tipped out. It does, however, make a difference to the uncertainty of measurement (see 'Uncertainty and errors' on p. 19), so it is good practice to record that you used the tare.

Recording data

All data should be recorded in tables. Before you start, think about what you are going to record and then draw up an appropriate table. Don't jot down readings on scraps of paper. You should ensure that:

- your table has a heading
- you draw lines with a ruler between the columns (and rows if necessary) of the table
- you give the **units** for each quantity (this can be done in column headings); the accepted way to give units is to use a slash (e.g. volume/cm^3)
- you record the reading from each instrument to the appropriate number of decimal places ('Reading instruments' above). If a thermometer has marks every 1°C, record readings as, for example, 10.5°C, 20.0°C. Do not forget the '.0', where appropriate
- you record all readings, *not* differences — for example, record the starting temperature and the final temperature, *not* the temperature rise or fall, which can be calculated from your data

An example of good recording is shown in Box 1 below.

Box 1: The temperature changes when zinc reacts with copper(II) sulfate solution

Preliminary data

Mass of zinc (using 'tare' on balance)	6.1 g
Volume of 1.00 mol dm^{-3} copper(II) sulfate solution (pipette)	25.00 cm^3

Temperature variation with time

Time/s	Temperature/°C	Time/s	Temperature/°C
0	20.5	300	47.0
30	20.5	330	46.5
60	20.5	360	46.0
90	20.5	390	45.5
120	20.5	420	45.0
150	20.5	450	44.5
210	44.0	480	44.0
240	48.0	510	43.5
270	47.5		

See Question 6 (p. 13) for an opportunity to plot these data on a graph.

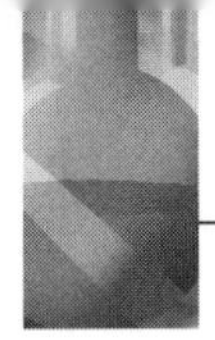

Question

(4) Point out the errors in the following example of recording data.
The data given below come from an experiment to determine the volume of a mole of hydrogen gas. Some magnesium ribbon is introduced into a burette that is nearly full of dilute hydrochloric acid and is upside-down in a beaker of water. The magnesium reacts with the acid and gives off hydrogen, which pushes the acid down the burette.

- **The mass of magnesium used was 0.035 g in the first experiment and 0.03 in the second.**
- **In the first experiment the volume in the burette changed by 30.0, in the second the burette readings were 45.3 and 18.65.**

Plotting graphs

Graphs are an excellent way of presenting information about how one variable changes with another.

If possible, plot relationships that should give straight lines. These are easy to test and information can be obtained from their gradients.

Notes on graph plotting

When carrying out an investigation, plot at least some graphs by hand. Not only will this show-off your graph-plotting skills, it is often easier to obtain fine detail from hand-plotted graphs.

- Decide the variables to be plotted.
- Decide whether the origin should be on your graph (two variables are only proportional if the straight line goes through the origin).
- Write a title — for example, 'The relationship between rate and temperature'.
- Choose scales so that you use most of the piece of graph paper and use a scale that is easy to read. Avoid strange scales (e.g. 5 units in three or four squares).
- Use an HB pencil.
- Label the axes with the quantity and unit — for example, time/s and rate/$cm^3 s^{-1}$.
- Plot the independent variable (the one *you* fix) on the *x*-axis and the dependent variable on the *y*-axis. Note that if the independent variable is not continuous (e.g. can only be 1, 2, 3 etc.) or is categoric (Experiment 1, Experiment 2 etc.) use a bar chart, *not* a graph. However, bar charts are seldom suited to A-level work.
- Plot the points carefully with small crosses '+' (see error bars below).
- Draw a smooth curve or the best straight line through the points. Do *not* join the points.

For examples see 'Reaction-rate graphs' in the Appendix (pp. 65–69).

Questions

(5) A reaction was carried out in which a gas was produced. The volume of gas was measured at 30-second intervals. The following results were obtained.

Plot a graph of these results and draw a line of best fit.

Time/s	Vol/cm^3
30	20
60	38
90	54
120	68
150	80
180	90
210	98
240	104
270	108
300	110
330	110

(6) Plot a graph of the data on 'temperature variation with time', given in Box 1 (p. 11).

Error bars

Note that the use of error bars is not required for AS and is not *essential* for A2.

- Consider making the lengths of the arms of the crosses you plot an indication of the uncertainty in the data. The accepted symbol is:

(see Figure 17 on p. 67). The arms of the crosses are called 'error bars'.

- If a straight line can be drawn that goes through all the error bars, then the relationship is linear to within the limits of uncertainty of the data.
- If a gradient is to be calculated, the 'best' and the 'worst' lines going through all the error bars should be drawn. The difference in the gradients of these two lines gives an indication of the uncertainty in the gradient.

Gradients

Important points about gradients include the following:

- The gradient is the slope of a curve.
- It is the **tangent** to a curve at the point concerned.
- In Figure 6 on p. 14, the gradient at the origin is the straight line that has the same slope as the curve at the origin, as shown.

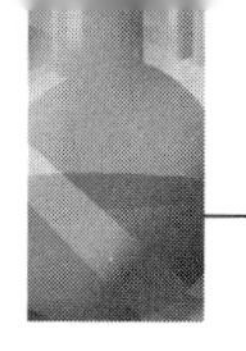

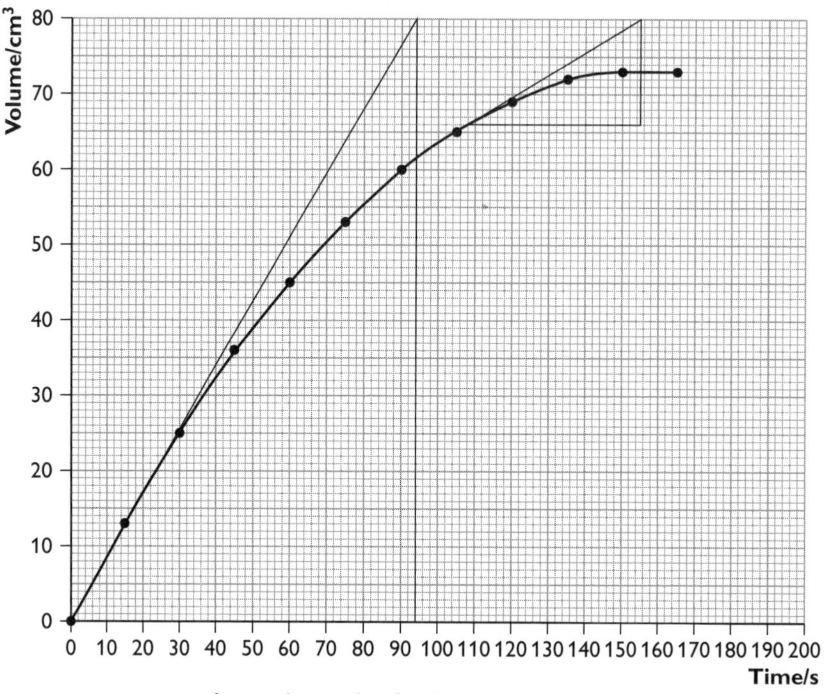

Figure 6 Graph of volume against time

- Draw a 'slope triangle' as large as you can (see Figure 6).
- The gradient is given by the change in y divided by the change in x. In Figure 6: gradient = 80/94 = 0.85 $cm^3 s^{-1}$.
- If the graph is a straight line, its slope does not vary. Draw a large 'slope triangle' and measure the change in y and the change in x.
- Be careful to note any standard form in the quantities on the graph — for example, the x-axis might be '$\times 10^{-3}$'.

Question

(7) Refer to the graph in Figure 6 and answer the following questions.

- **(a) What is the gradient at 110 seconds? (See the other triangle shown on the graph)**
- **(b) What is the gradient at 160 seconds?**
- **(c) Draw a triangle and calculate the gradient at 90 seconds.**

Making observations

While doing AS tasks (skill IV) and carrying out investigations, you have to make observations of chemical changes. This is not as easy as it sounds. You will need practice, which you will get by carrying out a variety of experiments during your course.

Note the following points:

- Always follow instructions carefully. In particular, be exact about the number of drops of reagents you have to add.
- If told to add 'dropwise' or 'drop by drop', do just that. Don't add a squirt.
- If told to shake the tube, do this by moving the tube from side to side quickly without spilling any of the contents. Do this thoroughly, until nothing further happens. Do not record events that are just a result of solutions not mixing properly, when they later do mix.
- If there is a colour change, record the starting and the finishing colours. Describe colours with just one shade — for example 'red' or 'brown' *not* 'a sort of dirty reddish brown colour'.
- Note that 'clear' means that you can see through the solution/mixture. It does not mean that it has no colour. You must say 'colourless'.
- Look out for the formation of a solid when two solutions are mixed. This is known as a precipitate, so use this word. If it is faint, you could describe it as, for example, 'a faint white precipitate'.
- Write observations *not* conclusions. If it fizzes, say so. Do not say 'gas given off'. If a brown coloration is formed say so. Do not say 'bromine produced' — even if it is.
- If two separate layers form, make sure that you say this. Describe the colour of each layer, making it clear which is the upper layer and which is the lower layer.
- Always heat test tubes carefully. Use a test-tube holder and move the test tube around in the flame. It is all too easy for the contents to splash out.
- If you are not sure you have seen everything that you should have, repeat the test, particularly if it is a quick one.

Question

(8) The following students did not score full marks for their observations, even though they probably saw all the things that happened. Write out their possible observations correctly.

(a) It went yellow, and then on adding cyclohexane an orange layer was formed on the top.

(b) On mixing, the solution went cloudy.

(c) On mixing, the solution became a murky sort of red/black colour.

Doing calculations

General rules for calculations are:

- Set them out neatly.
- Explain your steps using words.
- In intermediate answers, keep at least one more significant figure than you will need at the end.

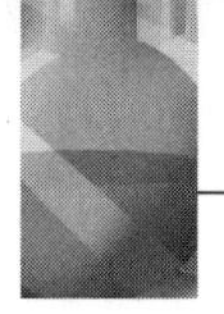

- When you give a final answer, remember:
  - **sign** (write + before a positive number if the answer *could* be minus)
  - **units**
  - **significant figures** (the same as the smallest number of significant figures in the data — or you could give the ± uncertainty if you have calculated it)
- In investigations, where there are many calculations that are similar, do not write each one out in full. Show one calculation in full with a full explanation in words. Then tabulate the results of the other calculations that have the same method. Consider using formulae on a spreadsheet if you can.

Significant figures

Significant figures are a quick way of indicating uncertainty. Thus, if a quantity is stated as '2', it is assumed to be between 1.5 and 2.5 and it has *one* significant figure. 2.0 (between 1.95 and 2.05) has *two* significant figures, and so on.

Note that 0.02 has *one* significant figure (this is more obvious if it is written in standard form 2×10^{-2}). 0.000002 also has one significant figure, whereas 0.200000 has six.

Significant figures are often confused with **decimal places**. Decimal places are the figures after the decimal point, whether these are zeros or numbers. For example, 0.02 and 0.20 both have two decimal places, but 0.02 has one significant figure and 0.20 has two.

Ambiguity arises in numbers greater than 1. For example, '100' could have one, two or three significant figures. Standard form removes the ambiguity — for example, 1.0×10^2 has two significant figures.

When doing a calculation involving measurements, look at the number of significant figures quoted. It will often be the same for all the data, in which case you should give your answer to the same number of significant figures. If there is variation, give your answer to the *smallest* number of significant figures given in the data.

Question

(9) (a) State the number of significant figures in each of the following:

5.0 2.10 0.047 0.0003 6.5430×10^2 250

(b) Give 15.465 to four, three and two significant figures.

(c) You are asked to calculate the number of moles in 20.0 cm^3 of a 0.050 mol dm^{-3} solution. The numerical answer comes to 0.001. How should you express this?

(d) You are asked to calculate the number of moles of ethanol in 4.600 g. The numerical answer comes to 0.1. How should you express this?

Calculations from equations (general)

The point here is that the numbers in front of formulae in equations indicate how many moles are reacting.

The rules are:

- Turn the mass of the given substance into moles.
- Use the ratio from the equation to calculate the moles of the required substance.
- Then, turn the moles back to masses.

Worked example

Calculate the mass of sodium carbonate formed when 16.8 g of sodium hydrogencarbonate is heated.
(From the Data Sheet, A_r: Na 23.0; C 12.0; H 1.0; O 16.0)

Answer

Equation: $2NaHCO_3 \rightarrow Na_2CO_3 + H_2O + CO_2$
M_r of $NaHCO_3 = 23.0 + 1.0 + 12.0 + 48.0 = 84.0$
moles of $NaHCO_3 = 16.8/84.0 = 0.200$ mol
The equation shows that 2 mol $NaHCO_3$ form 1 mol of Na_2CO_3.
Therefore, 0.200 mol $NaHCO_3$ will form 0.100 mol Na_2CO_3.
This has a mass of **10.6 g** (M_r of Na_2CO_3 = 106.0).

A slight variation on this uses the fact that *one mole of molecules of a gas occupies 24 dm³ at room temperature and pressure*. Note that you will be given this information when it is required.

So, in the worked example above, to calculate the volume of carbon dioxide formed, note that the same number of moles of CO_2 are formed as Na_2CO_3, i.e. 0.10. Thus, $0.10 \times 24 =$ **2.4 dm³** of gas would be formed at room temperature and pressure.

If we are dealing with *all gases* the volumes are proportional to the moles reacting. For example, for methane burning:

$$CH_4(g) + 2O_2(g) \rightarrow CO_2(g) + 2H_2O(g)$$

Here one volume of methane (say 1.0 dm³) would react with two volumes of oxygen (2.0 dm³) to form one volume (1.0 dm³) of carbon dioxide.

Question

(10) A student reacts 10.6 g of sodium carbonate, Na_2CO_3 with 100 cm³ of 1.0 mol dm⁻³ hydrochloric acid.

(a) Write the equation for the reaction.

(b) Show by calculation which reagent is in excess.

(c) Calculate the volume of carbon dioxide that would be formed at room temperature and pressure. (Volume of 1 mole of gas at room temperature and pressure is 24 dm³).

(d) The sodium chloride solution formed is evaporated. Calculate the mass of sodium chloride that is formed.

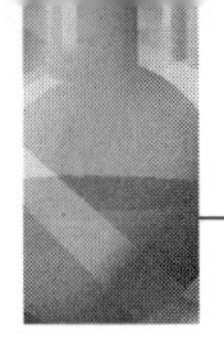

Titration calculations

The purpose of doing a titration is to find the volumes of solutions that react. If you are given the concentration of one solution, you can calculate the concentration of the other solution.

- First, write a chemical equation for the reaction (or look at a given equation).
- Then, work out the number of moles of one of the reagents (reagent 1) from the data given. Use **equation 1** below to do this:

$$\text{moles} = \frac{\text{volume} \times \text{molar concentration}}{1000} \quad \textbf{equation 1}$$

- Use the chemical equation to work out the number of moles of reagent 2 that react with reagent 1. Use this to calculate the moles of reagent 2.
- Rearrange **equation 1** to calculate the concentration of reagent 2.

Worked example

25.00 cm^3 of 0.200 mol dm^{-3} sodium hydroxide solution react with 21.30 cm^3 of sulfuric acid. Calculate the concentration of the acid.

Answer

equation: $H_2SO_4 + 2NaOH \rightarrow Na_2SO_4 + 2H_2O$

moles sodium hydroxide = $25.00 \times 0.200/1000 = 5.00 \times 10^{-3}$ mol

equation shows that 2 mol of NaOH react with 1 mol H_2SO_4

so moles $H_2SO_4 = 2.50 \times 10^{-3}$ mol

concentration of sulfuric acid = $2.50 \times 10^{-3} \times 1000/21.30 = 0.117$ mol dm^{-3}

The final answer is given to 3 significant figures, since some data are given to 3 s.f. and some to 4.s.f.

Questions

(11) 25.00 cm^3 of 0.0200 mol dm^{-3} sodium carbonate solution react with 27.15 cm^3 of hydrochloric acid. Calculate the concentration of the acid.

(12) 25.00 cm^3 of a sodium hydrogencarbonate solution react with 24.30 cm^3 of 0.100 mol dm^{-3} sulfuric acid. Calculate the concentration of the sodium hydrogencarbonate solution.

(13) 25.00 cm^3 of a solution of citric acid react with 24.65 cm^3 0.100 mol dm^{-3} sodium hydroxide solution. The solution of citric acid was made up by dissolving 5.00 g of impure citric acid in water, and making up to 250 cm^3. Citric acid reacts with sodium hydroxide as shown in the equation below:

$$C_6H_8O_7 + 3NaOH \rightarrow C_6H_5O_7Na_3 + 3H_2O$$

Calculate the percentage purity of the citric acid in the sample.

Uncertainties and errors

Uncertainty

Apparatus can never be read with perfect precision. For example, when reading a burette as 21.25 cm^3, this is really saying 'it's not 21.30 cm^3 and it's not 21.20 cm^3'. This is therefore written as 21.25 ± 0.05 cm^3, the 0.05 cm^3 being the **uncertainty** of the measurement.

As a general rule, the uncertainty can be taken to be the same size as the smallest unit that can be measured on the instrument (half the smallest division marked on the instrument).

- Thus, for a burette, the uncertainty is ±0.05 cm^3.
- For a thermometer calibrated in units of 1°C, read to the nearest 0.5°C, it is ±0.5°C.
- For a balance reading to 0.1 g, it is ±0.05 g.
- The uncertainty in a given value (e.g. a constant or a molar concentration) can be taken to be *half* of the last place given. Thus, a constant 22.4 is assumed to be 22.4 ± 0.05 (larger than 22.35 and smaller than 22.45). A molar concentration of 2.00 mol dm^{-3} is assumed to be 2.00 ± 0.005 mol dm^{-3} (larger than 1.995 and smaller than 2.005).

The **percentage uncertainty** is the uncertainty expressed as a percentage of the reading being taken.

Thus, measuring 12.0 cm^3 on a measuring cylinder calibrated to 0.1 cm^3, the percentage uncertainty is:

$$\frac{0.05 \times 100}{12.0} = 0.4\%$$

Measuring 25.0 cm^3 on the same measuring cylinder, the percentage uncertainty is:

$$\frac{0.05 \times 100}{25.0} = 0.2\%$$

So the percentage uncertainty (for the same instrument) gets smaller as the amount measured gets larger. This is why titration results are usually 20 cm^3 or larger — to keep the percentage uncertainty reasonably small.

For apparatus made to make a single measurement, the uncertainty depends on how the glassware has been made. Thus:

- the uncertainty in measuring 250.0 cm^3 with a standard flask is 0.2 cm^3 (0.08%)
- the uncertainty in measuring 25.0 cm^3 with a pipette is 0.06 cm^3 (0.2%)

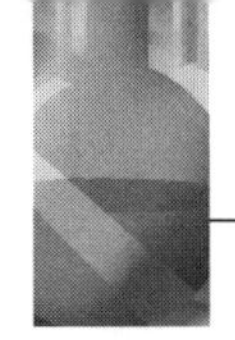

Question

(14) State the uncertainty and the percentage uncertainty in measuring each of the following:

(a) 25 cm^3 using a 250 cm^3 measuring cylinder, marked in 2 cm^3 intervals
(b) 25 cm^3 using a 100 cm^3 measuring cylinder, marked in 1 cm^3 intervals
(c) 25 cm^3 using a 25 cm^3 measuring cylinder, marked in 0.5 cm^3 intervals
(d) 25 cm^3 using a measuring cylinder, marked in 0.1 cm^3 intervals
(e) 40°C on a thermometer marked in 1°C units
(f) 40°C on a thermometer marked in 0.1°C units
(g) 15.25 g on a balance that reads to 0.01 g
(h) a solution with concentration quoted as 3.0 mol dm^{-3}

Combining uncertainties

Note that combining uncertainties is *not* required at AS and is not *essential* at A2.

When readings with uncertainties are multiplied or added together, what is the overall uncertainty in the final answer?

Multiplying and dividing quantities with uncertainties

Here, a simple rule is to *add* the percentage uncertainties.

Worked example

485 ± 1 cm^3 of water is heated through 16 ± 1°C
amount of energy transferred to the water is 485 × 4.18 × 16 = 32 436.8 J
percentage uncertainties are:
volume 1 × 100/485 = 0.2%   temperature 1 × 100/16 = 6.3%
The uncertainty in the specific heat capacity, 4.18 can be taken to be 0.005 (half the last decimal place) so the percentage is 0.005 × 100/4 = 0.125%, smaller than the other two; if this were not the case, another decimal place for the specific heat capacity could be looked up.
total percentage uncertainty = 0.2 + 6.3 + 0.125 = 7% (one significant figure is sufficient)
7% of 32 436.8 is 2000 (to 1 s.f.)
energy transferred = 32 000 ± 2000 J
(Note that we do not write 32 436.8 ± 2000, since the 436.8 has no meaning when the uncertainty is 2000.)
The calculation also shows that, if the precision of any apparatus is to be improved, it is the thermometer, not the measuring cylinder, that should be considered.

Adding and subtracting quantities with uncertainties

The rule here is to add the **actual** uncertainties (*not* the percentage uncertainties).

For example, if a volume is read from a burette, with an uncertainty of 0.05 cm^3 in each reading, the uncertainty in the volume is 0.05 + 0.05 = 0.1 cm^3.

If the initial and final volumes are 1.05 ± 0.05 cm^3 and 25.45 ± 0.05 cm^3, the volume used is 24.4 ± 0.1 cm^3, which is still fairly precise (uncertainty 0.4%). However, if the second volume had been 2.15 ± 0.05 cm^3, the volume used would have been 1.1 ± 0.1 cm^3 (uncertainty 10%).

Note that, when a balance is being used, the uncertainty is *once* that of a single reading if the 'tare' method is used (see p. 11), but *twice* that uncertainty if two weighings are used.

Worked example

A sample of potassium hydrogencarbonate ($KHCO_3$, M_r = 100.1 ± 0.05) was weighed in a boat. The solid was dissolved in water, transferred to a 250 cm^3 volumetric flask and the solution made up to the mark. The empty boat was weighed. The solution was used to standardise a solution of hydrochloric acid. Calculate the concentration of the acid and the uncertainty in this value.

Answer

mass of boat with $KHCO_3$ = 15.56 ± 0.005 g
mass of empty boat = 5.48 ± 0.005 g
volume of $KHCO_3$ pipetted out = 25.0 ± 0.06 cm^3
titration result with HCl = 21.3 ± 0.1 cm^3
mass of $KHCO_3$ = 10.08 ± 0.01 g (*add actual uncertainties since subtracting quantities*)

molar concentration of $KHCO_3$ = vol × 1000/(M_r × 250) = $\frac{10.09 \times 1000}{100.1 \times 250}$ = 0.403 mol dm^{-3}

percentage uncertainties are 0.1% in 10.08; 0.05% in 100.1; 0.08% in 250 (*the value for a 250 cm^3 volumetric flask — see above*)

total uncertainty (*add percentage uncertainties since multiplying and dividing*) *= 0.23%*

so, molar concentration = 0.403 ± 0.001 mol dm^{-3}
$KHCO_3$ and HCl react 1:1 by moles
so, concentration of HCl = 0.403 × 25.0/21.3 = 0.473

percentage uncertainties are concentration: 0.403, 0.2%; pipette: 0.2% (*see above*) *and 21.3, 0.5%*

total uncertainty = 1%

concentration = 0.473 ± 0.005 mol dm^{-3}

Here, all the uncertainties in the quantities are of similar size, so it is hardly worth improving just one of them. Note that, if 'whole number' values had been taken for M_r, the uncertainty would have been 0.5%, which would have made a major contribution to the overall uncertainty.

Note also that, when uncertainties are given they should be used (rather than significant figures), but that here the 'significant figure' method would give a similar value (3 s.f.) for the answer.

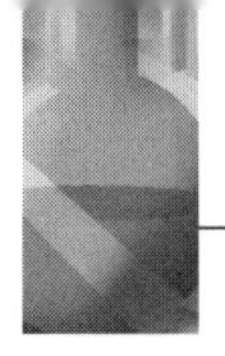

Questions

(15) A student carries out a titration in which the concentration of the reagent is given as 0.40 mol dm^{-3}. The titration result is 26.30 cm^3 and a 25.0 cm^3 pipette is used. Which quantity contributes most to the overall uncertainty — the concentration, the burette reading or the pipette reading?

(16) A student weighs 0.59 g of powder on a balance that reads to 0.01 g, by weighing a boat full, then empty. Quote the mass, showing the uncertainty as '±'.

(17) A student weighs 0.05 g of powder on a balance that reads to 0.01 g, by weighing a boat full, then empty. What is the percentage uncertainty in the mass of 0.05 g?

Accuracy and precision

Accuracy and **precision** are not the same. What we have been talking about so far is precision, which is to do with the **repeatability** of results.

Accuracy can only be determined if the **true value** of a quantity is known. In science, knowing the 'true value' is impossible, because a scientist may come along later and show that the value is wrong. However, as our experiments are unlikely to show this, we can assume that values given in data books and tables are correct.

Suppose that we carry out an experiment in which the result is 205 ± 1 (arbitrary units). This, in terms of school practical work, is quite precise — we would probably pat ourselves on the back for keeping the uncertainty as low as 0.5%.

Now we look up the value in a data book. If the data book value is 205.9, our experiment is accurate, i.e. we have achieved the 'accepted' value within the limits of uncertainty. Any value between 204 and 206 would mean that the experiment is accurate. This is also true if the value is up to 206.4, because this rounds down to 206. However, if the accepted value is 210, we have either not calculated the uncertainty correctly or some other factor is responsible. The experiment remains precise but it is *not* accurate.

If the experimental result had been 200 ± 50, the experiment is much less precise. However, provided that the accepted value lies between 150 and 250, the experiment is accurate.

Percentage error

If the accepted value of a quantity is known, the percentage error is given by:

$$\frac{\text{difference between experimental result and accepted result}}{\text{accepted result}} \times 100$$

Systematic error

If the experiment is not accurate, the deviation from the accepted value must be due to systematic error.

Systematic error can be divided into three types:

- operator error
- apparatus error
- method error

These are the kind of things to be discussed as 'limitations' in the evaluation section of your investigation.

Operator error

This does *not* mean, for example, 'I made a mistake reading the balance' or 'I overshot the end point'. Consider a digital timer. It may measure in 0.01 s intervals, meaning the uncertainty of measurement is 0.005 s. However, humans cannot react at that speed so it will be operator error that determines the precision of the timing, not uncertainty.

Other situations involve, for example:

- an end point that is difficult to judge
- a reading that is moving and difficult to read (e.g. a fluctuating temperature)

Apparatus error

It may be that the pipette you have has the 25.0 cm^3 line in the wrong place. This is unlikely but possible. If this were the case, it would throw all your readings. They would still be as precise as before but their accuracy would suffer.

If you place several thermometers in a well-stirred beaker of water (therefore presumably at the same temperature), they may read differently. However, the differences in the temperature measured on all the thermometers are likely to be much more accurate.

However, do *not* blame your apparatus without real evidence and certainly do not say 'all our school apparatus is old and unreliable', or words to that effect.

'Heat losses' ('transfer of energy to the surroundings' as physicists would prefer) are common in thermochemical experiments. They can be minimised — for example, by plotting a 'cooling graph' and extrapolating to the theoretical temperature. They can also be minimised by using much more sophisticated apparatus.

Method error

If you have to start a reaction, replace a bung and start a stopwatch all at the same time, there is bound to be an error. If possible, alter the method to avoid this.

Method errors often involve operations that should be instantaneous (e.g. mixing solutions) but which in reality take a finite time.

If you cannot see clearly an end point in a titration, try adding slightly more indicator. If this still does not work, try a different indicator.

When doing investigations, there is also the issue of having to take readings over a number of laboratory sessions on different days. Good planning should mean that you have sufficient solution in one batch to do all your experiments, but if anything goes

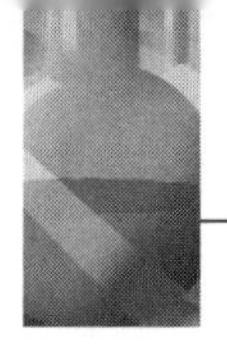

wrong and you have to use a different batch, make a careful note of which results were taken with which batch and comment only if there are significant differences. Changes in room temperature may also affect results between sessions.

Example: measuring enthalpy changes of combustion by burning fuels

Cause of systematic error	Way of minimising error
Heat losses from the apparatus (heat transferred to the surroundings)	Cover the top of the beaker; more screens; lag the sides of the beaker
Heat losses to the beaker	Use a metal calorimeter (most metals have a lower specific heat capacity than glass)
Evaporation of the fuel, especially when weighing the burner	Place a cap on the burner
Incomplete combustion of the fuel	Hard to eradicate without more specialist apparatus

Typical uncertainties in the measurements are shown in the table below.

Quantity	Possible reading	Apparatus	Percentage uncertainty
Temperature change	20°C	Thermometer — two readings to ±0.5°C	1/20 = 5%
Volume of water	200 cm^3	Measuring cylinder ±2 cm^3	2/200 = 1%
Mass of liquid	1 g	Balance — two readings ±0.005 g	0.01/1 = 1%

Thus, it would be worth using a thermometer accurate to 0.1°C to reduce the overall uncertainty.
However, if the result is more than 7% away from the Data Book value, it is systematic errors that are likely to dominate.

Questions

(18) Two students measure the enthalpy change of combustion of a liquid by the same method, each measuring it several times. The units are kJ mol^{-1}. Their results were:

- **Student A: –2890, –2870, –2860 estimated uncertainty ±30**
- **Student B: –3400, –3500, –3450 estimated uncertainty ±50**

The accepted answer, from a data book, is –3780 kJ mol^{-1}.

(a) State which set of results is the more precise. Explain your answer.

(b) State which set of results is the more accurate. Explain your answer.

(c) Would you advise either student to use apparatus with a smaller uncertainty, or to take some other route to get more accurate results?

(19) The concentration of a solution is measured as 0.020 ± 0.002 mol dm^{-3}.
The solution was made up to be 0.025 ± 0.001 mol dm^{-3}.
Are these results consistent? Give a reason.

Interpreting observations

AS examination papers ask specific questions about the interpretation of observations (see p. 45).

In investigations, remember the following:

- You may have more or less confidence in your observations. This corresponds to the uncertainty in a piece of numerical data.
- An observation is *reliable* if:
  - several repeats give the same result
  - it results in a definite change (e.g. not just a faint cloudiness)
- An observation is *valid* if it enables you to draw meaningful conclusions. You may make observations as you do an experiment that ultimately turn out not to be valid, though you were not sure of this at the time. There is no reason not to record these observations, but do make it clear that you realise they are not valid with respect to your conclusions.

For an example, see Skill D, p. 55.

Practical techniques

Making up solutions

You have to do this in many practicals, particularly investigations.

The method

First, calculate the mass of substance you need to weigh out. For example, to make 250 cm^3 of a 0.0100 mol dm^{-3} solution, you need $250 \times 0.0100/1000 = 2.50 \times 10^{-3}$ mol. Multiply this by the M_r of the substance to work out the mass.

- Dissolve the substance in about 100 cm^3 distilled (deionised) water in a beaker. Use a glass rod to stir and break up lumps of solid. If possible, avoid heating.
- Pour the solution into a volumetric (standard) flask (Figure 7) using a small funnel. A volumetric flask has just one calibration at, for example, 100.0 cm^3 or 250.0 cm^3.

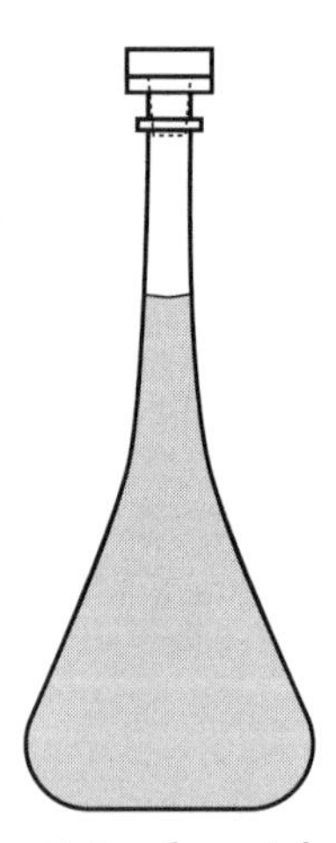

Figure 7 A volumetric flask

- Rinse the beaker and the funnel with distilled water, so that all the rinsings go into the volumetric flask.
- Add distilled water to the flask until the level reaches the bottom of the neck. Then add distilled water using a plastic dropping pipette until the meniscus just touches the mark.
- Stopper the flask and invert it several times to mix the contents.

Note that the uncertainty of a 250 cm^3 volumetric flask is 0.2 cm^3 (0.08%).

Question

(20) A student makes the following statements about the above method. Point out the errors.

(a) 'It's quicker to put the solid straight into the volumetric flask and dissolve it there. I can always heat it if necessary.'
(b) 'It doesn't matter if the solid hasn't all dissolved when I make it up to the mark, it will dissolve when I shake it.'
(c) 'If I overshoot the mark when adding water, it doesn't matter — it's only water and I can suck it out again.'
(d) 'It would be quicker to measure out exactly 250 cm^3 water in a volumetric flask, then add it to the solid in a beaker and stir it.'

Diluting solutions

If you need to dilute solutions precisely, use the following method:

- Estimate the volume of diluted solution that you will need for the experiment you have designed. Make sure that you have a volumetric flask of this volume.
- Calculate the volume of undiluted solution you will need ('old volume'), using the expression shown below, which indicates that the number of moles do not change:

  new volume × new concentration = old volume × old concentration

- Measure out the volume of undiluted solution in the most precise way you can, using a graduated pipette or a burette.
- Run this volume into the volumetric flask you selected.
- Make the flask up to the mark with distilled water and invert the flask to mix its contents.

Questions

(21) (a) A student has a 0.100 mol dm^{-3} solution. What does the student need to do to make 250 cm^3 of a 0.00500 mol dm^{-3} solution?
(b) Calculate the uncertainty in the 0.00500 value as ±.

(22) A student has a 0.50 mol dm^{-3} solution and wants to make a 0.050 mol dm^{-3} solution. The method adopted is to pipette out 10 cm^3 of solution and add this to 100 cm^3 water (from a volumetric flask) in a beaker. Calculate the actual concentration of the solution formed.

Doing titrations

Titrations measure precisely the volumes of solutions that react with each other.

The use of titrations is common in school chemistry and they are still used in industrial and research chemistry. They enable precise (low uncertainty) work to be done in the school laboratory and they test your ability to follow instructions and to work carefully and accurately.

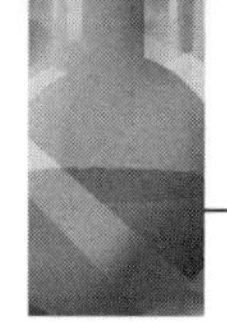

You will practise doing titrations in activities such as:

- determining how much iron there is in a sample of iron compound
- finding the concentration of an acid solution
- determining which is the most cost-effective bleach
- investigating the reaction between bromine and hexane
- carrying out an aspirin assay
- determining how much iron there is in dried thyme

The apparatus for titrations

The apparatus for carrying out a titration is shown in Figure 8.

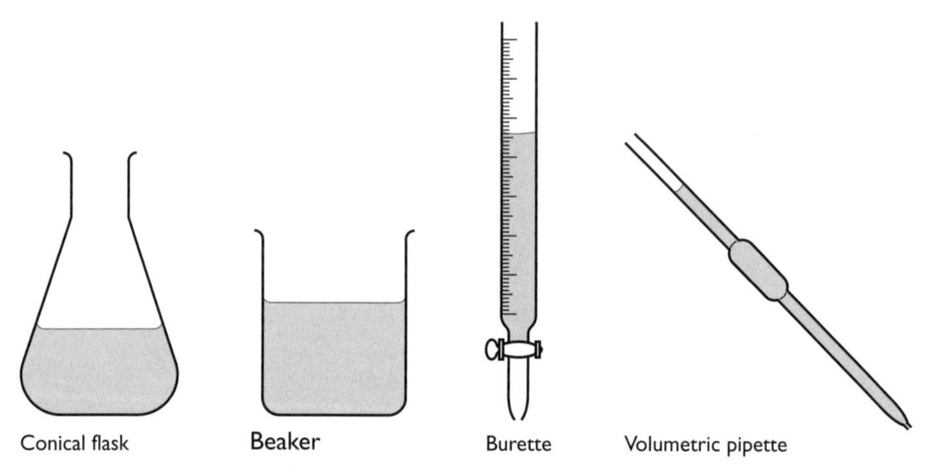

Figure 8 Apparatus for a titration

Conical flasks are so-called because they are shaped like a cone. They are used to contain the solution that is to be pipetted (the conical shape allows the pipette to reach all the contents) and the solution that is to be titrated, since they can be swirled without the solution splashing out.

Beakers are used to contain the solution that is placed in the burette. It is easier to pour out of a beaker. Beakers and conical flasks may have volumes marked on them, but these are only rough values.

Burettes are graduated tubes used to run one solution into another. They are calibrated (marked) with zero at the top, so that the reading gets larger as the solution flows out. The burette is held in a stand, usually a wooden or plastic one as it is easy to over-tighten a metal clamp and crack the glass. Your teacher will show you how to clamp your burette.

Pipettes come in various shapes and sizes. A pipette that is used for titration is called a **volumetric pipette**. This has just one graduation, usually 25.0 cm^3 or 10.0 cm^3.

It is *compulsory* to use a **pipette filler** to suck up solutions. A pipette filler is not illustrated because schools and colleges use different varieties. You will be shown how to use the particular pipette filler provided.

Procedure for carrying out a titration

(1) Collect a beaker, two conical flasks, a volumetric pipette, a burette and stand, a test tube, a small funnel and a white tile.

(2) The beaker is to hold the solution that will go in the burette. Rinse it with distilled water, and then with a little of the solution it will contain. Then partially fill it with about 150 cm^3 of this solution.

(3) One conical flask is to hold the solution that is to go in the pipette. Rinse the flask with distilled water and then with a little of the solution it will contain. Then partially fill it with about 150 cm^3 of this solution.

(4) Rinse the burette with the solution from the beaker. Place the burette in its stand with a small filter funnel in the top. Ensure the tap is closed. Then fill the burette to near the top, but do not try to get the reading exactly to zero. Run a little solution through the tap into a test tube. This fills the tap and ensures that there are no air bubbles.

(5) Rinse the pipette with solution from the conical flask. Rinse the second conical flask (the titration flask) with distilled (deionised) water.

(6) Using a pipette filler, transfer the exact volume of solution from the conical flask into the titration flask.

If necessary, practise using a pipette filler with a pipette and water. If you have a leaky pipette filler, get used to sucking up solution to well above the mark and then taking the filler off the pipette and rapidly placing your index finger over the end of the pipette. This should make the lowering of the level to the mark much easier to control.

Do *not* blow out the last little bit of solution from the pipette, but touch the pipette on the solution in the titration flask when it has emptied out. Pipettes drained in this way deliver the correct volume.

(7) Place the titration flask on a white tile below the burette. Add about five drops of indicator to the titration flask and remove the funnel from the top of the burette. (Note that some titrations are 'self indicating' and do not require an indicator.)

(8) Read the burette, to the nearest 0.05 cm^3, reading from the bottom of the meniscus. Read the burette at eye level (move the burette to do this if necessary, don't climb up) and hold a piece of white paper behind the burette to make it easier to read. Record the reading in a table (see below).

(9) Run the solution from the burette into the titration flask until the indicator just changes colour. You may overshoot the end point, so this is a 'trial' titration. Read the final volume in the burette. Record the reading in your table and label it 'trial'.

(10) Rinse out the titration flask with distilled (deionised) water. Repeat stages 6 to 8. Then run in solution from the burette to within 1 cm^3 of your trial result. Then proceed to add the solution drop by drop, swirling the flask between each addition. Stop when the indicator just changes colour. Read the burette and record the reading in your table.

(11) Repeat stage 10 until you have **concordant results**, i.e. results that are within 0.1 cm^3 of each other. You should have at least two, preferably three, concordant results. (Note that 0.1 cm^3 is acceptable for most titrations that you are likely to meet at AS. In an A2 investigation, the end point may not be so clear and you may decide to accept results that are less close together.)

(12) Record all your results in a table similar to that shown below.

	Trial	First	Second	Third	Etc.
Final burette reading/cm^3	26.20	26.45	26.65	25.20	
Initial burette reading/cm^3	0.15	1.35	1.40	0.10	
Titre/cm^3	26.05	25.10	25.25	25.10	

Some important points to note include:

- If you record the burette readings in the way shown in the table, you have a simple subtraction sum to do. The word 'titre' is the term used for the volume of solution that has been run out of the burette.
- Units must be given for all readings and readings should be to two decimal places, with the second decimal place being either zero or 5.
- The first reading is not exactly zero. It is difficult to fill a burette to exactly 0.00. However, if one of your readings *is* zero, it must be recorded as 0.00.
- It is usual to ignore the trial run and any results that are not concordant. Then average the other results.
- For the example given in the table, the average is calculated as:

$$\text{average} = \frac{21.70 + 21.75 + 21.70}{3} = 21.72\,\text{cm}^3$$

Unless otherwise instructed, give answers to titrations to two decimal places.

Questions

(23) Explain what you would expect to happen to the value of the titre obtained (compared with the 'correct' value) in each of the following circumstances:

(a) A student rinses out the burette with water only, and the pipette with the solution it is to contain.

(b) A student rinses out the pipette with water only, and the burette with the solution it is to contain.

(c) A student rinses the titration flask out with distilled water and does not empty it thoroughly before doing the titration.

(d) A student blows out the last drop of liquid from the pipette.

(e) A student does not touch the pipette on the surface of the solution in the titration flask at the end of pipetting.

(f) A student leaves the funnel in the top of the burette while doing the titration.

(g) A student rinses down the side of the titration flask with distilled water during the titration.

(24) A student records titration results as shown in the table. Re-draw the table, correcting the errors.

Start (cm^3)	0	0	0.15	0.13
Finish (cm^3)	26	25.4	25.55	25.55
Volume	26	25.4	25.45	25.42

Organic preparations

You carry out organic preparations at AS in such activities as 'Making a halogeno-alkane' (preparing and purifying an organic liquid) and 'Oxidation of ethanol', and at A2 in 'Preparation of aspirin' and 'Taking nylon apart' (preparation and purification of an organic solid). You may wish to prepare and purify compounds as part of your investigation.

Preliminaries

You have to work out the amounts of substance that you need. Do a mole calculation, but remember that the percentage yield of many organic preparations is often no more than 40% (see p. 35).

You will probably have a 'recipe' for the method, although you may need to develop this and design variations for your investigation. You must have any variations checked by your teacher — apparatus is expensive as well as potentially dangerous.

Heating under reflux

Refluxing (see Figure 9) uses a water condenser mounted vertically above a heated flask.

- The liquid in the flask boils and then condenses at the 'reflux ring'.
- It is useful for slow reactions (most organic reactions are slow) with volatile reactants and products that would otherwise escape.
- It is also useful because many organic liquids are flammable.
- Note that the water should enter at the *lower* connector and come out at the top. This ensures that the condenser is full of water and that only a gentle flow of water is necessary.
- The top of the condenser must *not* be stoppered, since there is expansion in the flask as the liquids are heated. All the liquids should condense; hence there is no need to stopper. Most laboratories have a tell-tale mark on the ceiling that shows what happens when a reflux condenser has been stoppered.

Take care when fitting rubber tubing to the connections on the condenser. Always hold the tube and glass close together to avoid the possibility of the joint breaking and the broken glass cutting you.

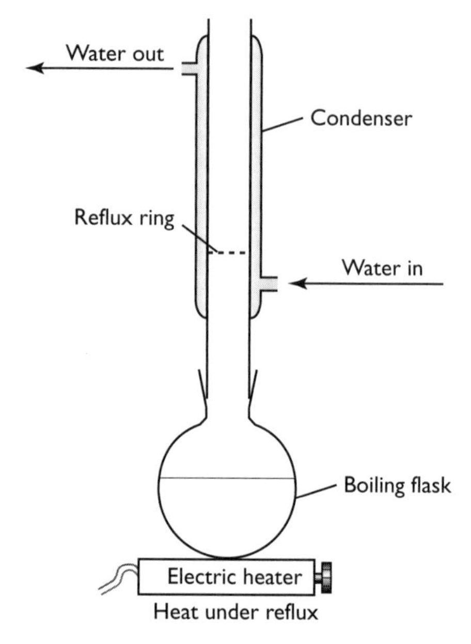

Figure 9 Heating under reflux

Distillation

Distillation is used to remove one liquid from a mixture of liquids (see Figure 10). The mixture concerned could be the result of refluxing.

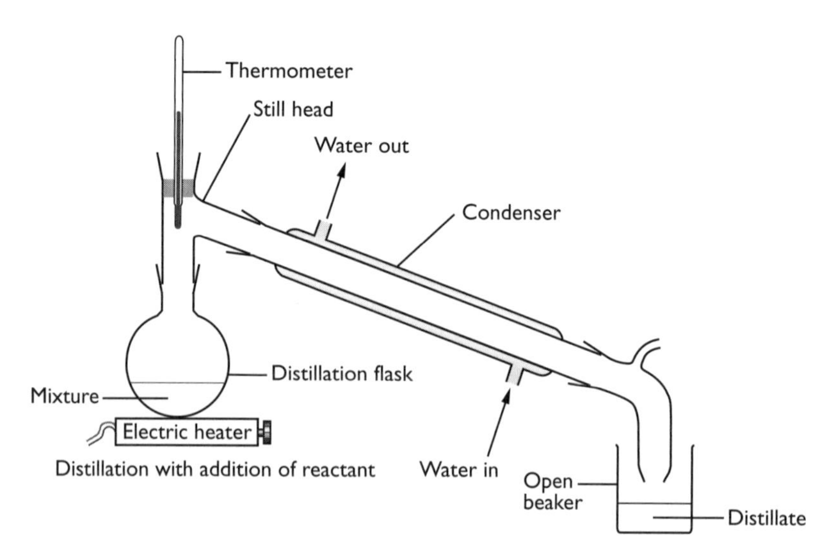

Figure 10 Distillation

The mixture is heated gently. The liquids reflux in turn round the thermometer (the ones with the lowest boiling points first) and are collected when their boiling points show on the thermometer.

Note that the water connections are again made so that water enters at the lower connector.

Purifying a liquid

The method is as follows:

- The liquid is shaken with various substances in a **separating funnel** (see Figure 11).
- The liquids are mixed in the separating funnel and shaken (cocktail-shaker style).
- If any gases are given off (e.g. when sodium hydrogen carbonate solution is used to remove acids) the funnel must be held upside down after shaking and the pressure released through the tap.
- The funnel is allowed to stand until the layers have separated. The two layers are then run off separately. Even if you are fairly sure which layer you need, it is good practice to collect both of them.
- If an organic layer has water as the main impurity, it can be dried by leaving it to stand over anhydrous sodium sulfate in a flask with a stopper. When all the water has been absorbed, the organic liquid will look clear, rather than cloudy. The mixture is then filtered through a mineral wool plug (organic liquids are soaked up by filter paper).
- A final distillation separates the liquid from any remaining impurities and enables its boiling point to be measured.

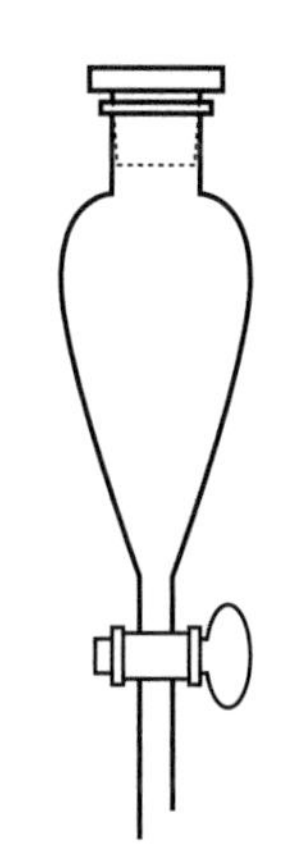

Figure 11 A separating funnel

Purifying a solid

Vacuum filtration

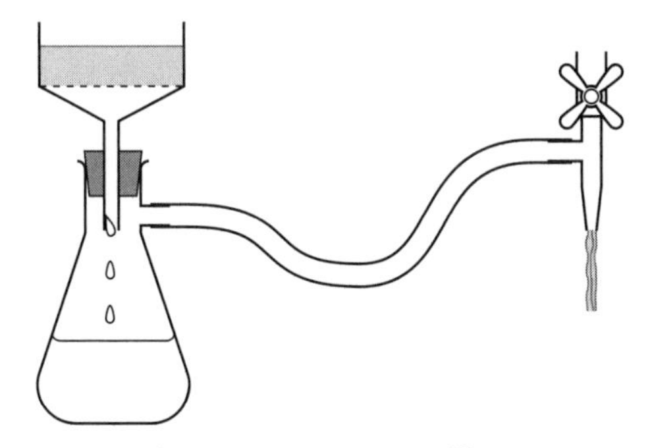

Figure 12 A vacuum filter

The solid is collected by vacuum filtration (see Figure 12):

- A moistened filter paper of the correct size is placed in the funnel. The vacuum pump is turned on and a suspension of the solid required is poured in.

- The solid collects on the filter paper. If the solvent is volatile, sucking air through the solid will dry it. Otherwise (if the solvent is water), the solid is first blotted dry and then dried in an oven.

The solid can be further purified by recrystallisation.

Recrystallisation

The method is as follows:

- A solvent has to be found in which the solid dissolves well when the solvent is hot but poorly when it is cold. A mixture of ethanol and water is often suitable.
- Set up a hot-water bath (a beaker half full of water over a Bunsen flame) containing two boiling tubes, one containing solvent, the other the solid.
- Add hot solvent to the solid in small portions and stir the mixture after each addition. Stop adding solvent immediately after a clear solution is formed (i.e. when the solid has dissolved in the minimum of hot solvent).
- If the hot solution contains any solid particles, filter it through a pre-heated vacuum filtration apparatus.
- Otherwise, leave the solution to cool and **recrystallise**. Scratching the inside of the tube with a glass rod creates nuclei that aid crystallisation.
- Using a vacuum filter, filter off the solid, then wash it with a little cold solvent and allow it to dry.
- Some solid will be lost in the process (since some always dissolves in the cold solvent) but the recrystallised solid will be purer than the starting solid.

Recrystallisation works because the impurities do not saturate the hot solvent, whereas the required substance does. Thus the impurities remain in solution when the solvent is cooled.

Measuring (or 'taking') melting points

There are a number of types of apparatus for determining melting points. You will be shown the one that is available to you. One type of apparatus is shown in Figure 13.

The method is as follows:

- Place a little finely powdered solid in a capillary tube and fix it (using an elastic band) to a thermometer.
- The liquid used is one that boils above the melting point of the solid.
- Heat the liquid and watch the solid in the capillary tube as the temperature rises. Suddenly the solid will turn to a clear liquid. Read the temperature — this is the melting point. If the solid melts over a range of temperatures, it is less pure and a **range** of temperatures should be recorded.

The melting point of a substance is *always* lowered by impurities (even if the impurity has a higher melting point). The theory behind this is complicated. If you want to find out more, look up 'eutectics' to get started.

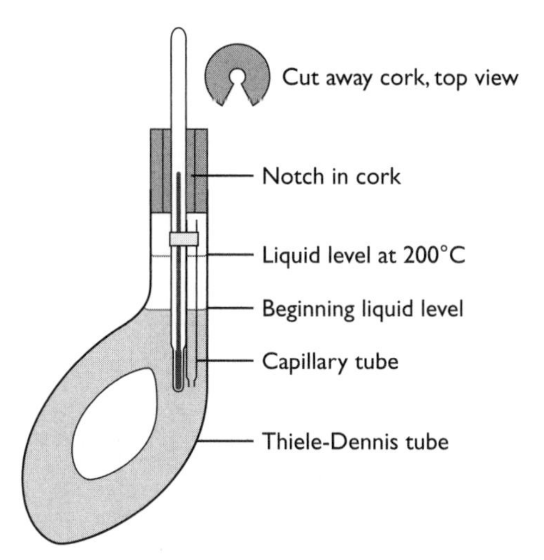

Figure 13 Apparatus for determining melting point

Chemists used to identify organic substances by preparing crystalline derivatives, which they then recrystallised, taking melting points and matching them against values in standard tables. Nowadays, spectroscopic methods are used.

Percentage yield

This is calculated as:

$$\text{percentage yield} = \frac{\text{actual mass of product obtained} \times 100}{\text{theoretical mass of product}}$$

The key thing is to look at the equation for the reaction. If you start with 1 mole of a reactant, how many moles of product is the maximum possible? For an organic reaction, this is usually 1 mole.

Work out the number of moles of the limiting reactant (the one that is not in excess). Then work out the number of moles of product this amount of reactant could produce.

Convert this into the maximum mass of product and substitute this into the equation above.

Questions

(25) A student is making bromobutane from butan-1-ol, using excess HBr. The yield is 3.2 g bromobutane from 5.0 g of butan-1-ol.

(a) Write a balanced equation for the reaction.

(b) Calculate the percentage yield.

(26) A student needs to make 12 g of phenylamine, $C_6H_5NH_2$, from nitrobenzene, $C_6H_5NO_2$, using excess inorganic reagents. Assuming the yield is 40%, calculate how much nitrobenzene is needed.

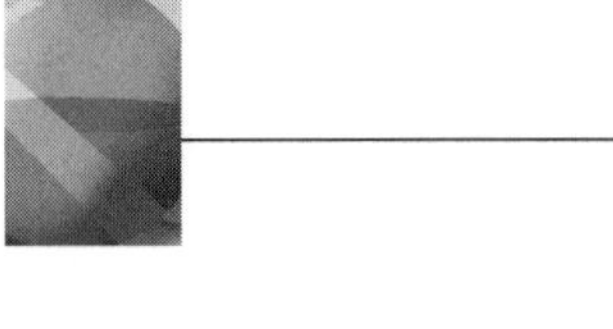

Colorimetry

A colorimeter is used to measure the concentration of a coloured substance in a solution.

It works by measuring the amount of light of a particular colour (determined by a coloured filter) that passes through a solution (see Figure 14). A spectrophotometer is a more sophisticated piece of apparatus that enables the wavelength of the colour to be chosen and used without the need to change filters.

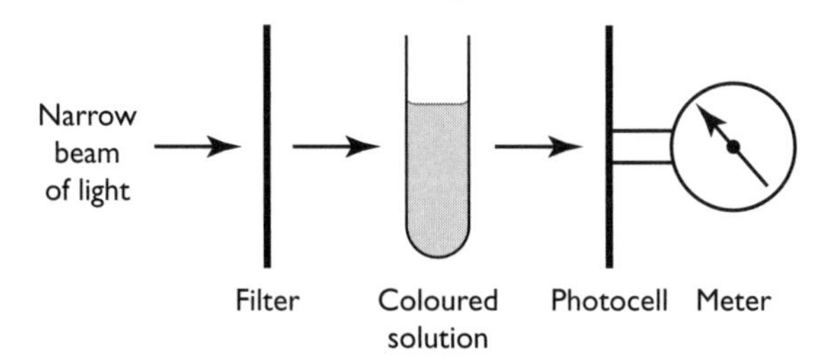

Figure 14 The essentials of a colorimeter

The colour of the filter is the complementary colour to the colour of the solution. For example, a green filter is used for a purple solution, because purple solutions absorb green light and transmit purple light. The meter reads the **absorbance** (the % light absorbed).

The best way to relate absorbance to concentration is to use a **calibration curve.**

The steps in measuring the concentration of a coloured solution with a colorimeter are:

- Select a suitable filter (complementary colour) for the colorimeter.
- Adjust absorbance to zero using a 'blank' tube containing water.
- Make up several standard solutions of the coloured substance ('standard' means of known concentration).
- Measure the absorbance for each of these solutions.
- Plot a graph of absorbance against concentration. This is the calibration curve.
- Find the absorbance for the solution of unknown concentration.
- Read off the concentration of the unknown from the calibration curve.

Thin-layer chromatography

A thin-layer plate consists of a layer of inert substance, such as alumina (aluminium oxide) on a plastic base. Paper chromatography can sometimes be substituted for thin layer but thin layer is faster because the solvent rises up the alumina layer more quickly.

The procedure is as follows:

- Using a pencil, draw a base line on a thin-layer plate, making sure it will be above the level of the solvent (see Figure 15).

- Using a capillary tube, place spots of known and unknown substances (in suitable solvents) on the base line. Place a little on at a time and allow it to dry before adding more. The spots should not exceed 2 mm in diameter.
- Place the plate in a **solvent** (so the spots are above the level of the solvent) in a beaker.
- Cover the beaker (clingfilm is useful for this).
- The solvent rises up the plate. When it is near the top, remove the plate and mark the final solvent level with pencil. This is called the 'solvent front'.
- Allow the plate to dry, and then treat the plate with a locating agent so that the spots show up. Suitable locating agents include ultraviolet light or iodine vapour (place the plate in a covered beaker with a few crystals of iodine).
- Spots of the same substance rise to the same characteristic height and, therefore, they can be identified.
- Alternatively, the R_f value ('retention factor') can be measured (see Figure 15). This can be looked up in tables as it is constant for a given substance under the same conditions.

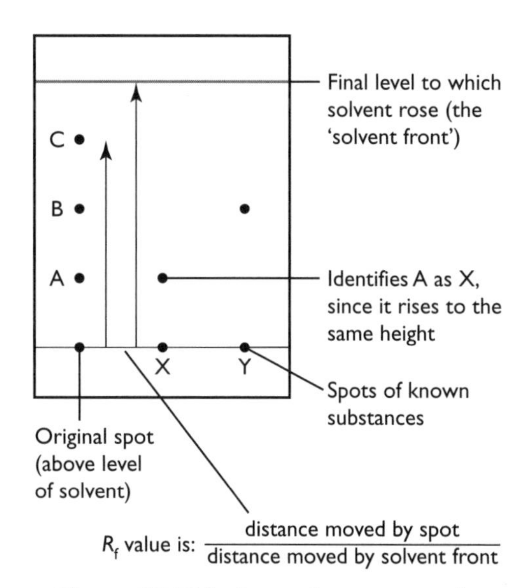

Figure 15 Thin-layer chromatography

Question

(27) (a) Give the approximate R_f value of compound C in the chromatogram in Figure 15.

(b) What extra experiment would you carry out to show that C was a compound Z?

The practical units

The first part of this section deals with the AS coursework Unit F333. For this you will be assessed in five skill areas by your teacher. These skill areas are:

- competence
- measurement
- analysis and evaluation
- observation
- interpretation

The second part deals with the A2 individual investigation Unit F336. You will be introduced to the individual investigation by your teacher, who will also tell you when this will take place — the most likely times are either the end of the autumn term or the beginning of the spring term.

F333: Chemistry in Practice

Skill I Competence

This is different from the other skills in that it takes into account all the practical work that you do over the AS year. This means that you should always do your best in practical work so that your teacher will be able to use the Skill I mark to reward you for good work at all times.

The specific areas that your teacher will be assessing are shown in the table below, together with some notes that include ways in which you can show good practical competence.

Practical activities for Skill I	Notes	Example activities
Carrying out titrations	Always try to get concordant results by doing titrations carefully and accurately (see pp. 27–30)	• How much iron is there in a sample of an iron compound? • Finding the concentration of an acid solution • Which is the most cost-effective bleach?
Making thermochemical measurements	Follow instructions carefully and try to get consistent results	• Measuring the enthalpy change of combustion of various fuels • Determining an enthalpy change of reaction
Carrying out qualitative experiments using test tubes	Follow the instructions and write down carefully what you see (see pp. 14–15)	• Investigating the chemistry of group 2 elements • Reactions of halogens and halides
Carrying out an experiment involving ICT	This might involve the use of data loggers or be a simpler experiment using a camera. Aim to get good results and make an interesting presentation if you are asked to	• Investigating visible emission spectra (presentation) • Determining the enthalpy change of a reaction (using a data logger) • Reactions of halogens and halides (presentation)
Preparing an organic compound	Set up your apparatus carefully and aim to get a good yield of product	• Cracking alkanes • Making a halogenoalkane • Oxidation of ethanol
Collaborating with other students in solving a problem	Always show respect for your colleagues in the class — help them (except in 'tasks') if they are not as good as you at doing practicals	• Which is the most cost-effective bleach? • How do concentration and temperature affect the rate of reaction?

Your teacher will make notes on how you perform throughout the AS course. Towards the end of the AS year you will be awarded a mark out of 6, based on the following general criteria:

- that you work safely all the time
- that you demonstrate well-developed manipulative skills in all practical procedures and resolve most problems without help
- that you demonstrate an organised approach to practical work and make all measurements and observations with great care and attention to detail

Some more general points arising out of the above are:

- Always work safely.
- Think before you start work, then try to work methodically through the practical.
- Keep your practical place clean and tidy at all times.
- Don't gossip.
- You should regard practical work as a chance to further your understanding of the subject, not as a break from the rigours of theory.
- Think about the results you obtain and how they fit into your understanding of the subject.
- If you come across a difficulty, think about it and try to solve it yourself. If you find you can't solve it, then ask your teacher, telling him or her what you have tried so far.

Skills II–V General

These skills are assessed by 'tasks' that are set in your lessons, on days chosen by your teacher.

Your teacher may warn you that a task is imminent and give you a general idea of the area it will cover. Heed these warnings and do some preparation. You must work on your own at these tasks and not communicate with other students.

Skills II and IV involve doing practical work and recording the results; skills III and V are theoretical papers that test your understanding of given results.

The only reference you are normally allowed is the Salters Data Sheet. The only part of this that is usually relevant is the periodic table, which gives the values of relative atomic masses and atomic numbers.

At the end of the lesson, your teacher will collect your work and mark it using a mark scheme provided by the examination board. This ensures that all students carrying out the task are marked to the same standard.

You will never again see what you have written, but your teacher may tell you in general terms how you have done and the areas you need to improve, so that you can do better in a similar task, if necessary.

If you do not perform to the expected standard, your teacher cannot give back the task to repeat or improve. Your teacher can, however, set you *another* task in the same skill area, which will be different but which will assess the same skill. There are three tasks available in each skill area each year.

Remember that not everyone can get full marks in every task. If you have not scored as many marks as you hoped, be guided by your teacher's advice on whether you need to take another task for the same skill area. Remember that time spent on repeats means that you have less time for the other skills and for the theory papers.

Skill II Measurement

The tasks here involve carrying out a practical that requires measurement. You will be given all the instructions but will be expected to be able to handle simple apparatus. You will have been taught how to do this before you do the task.

You will be given about 1 hour for the task, but you may not need all this time.

The task sheet will tell you what to do. Follow the instructions carefully.

Make sure that you:
- measure volumes carefully, reading at the bottom of the meniscus
- read apparatus to half the smallest unit to which it is calibrated, e.g. read a thermometer calibrated in degrees to the nearest half degree and read a measuring cylinder calibrated every 2 cm^3 to the nearest 1 cm^3 (see p. 9)
- record your results in a table; quote *all* data to the precision described above (see p. 11 for more detail on tables)

Skill III Analysis and evaluation

This skill is assessed by a theoretical task. You have 1 hour to complete the task, but you might well finish early.

The task could be a follow-up to the Skill II task you did previously.

If your teacher tells you the area of chemical theory that is being tested in the task, you should revise this using your own notes and books such as the student unit guides for Units F331 and F332, published by Philip Allan Updates.

The task will involve analysis of numerical data obtained from practical work. Analysis may involve doing calculations or plotting graphs, so read the relevant sections in this book.

Evaluation could involve working out or discussing uncertainties and systematic errors. Sections in this book cover these topics (see pp. 19–24).

Skill III and examination technique

The examination technique points that you have learned for the theory papers are also important here.

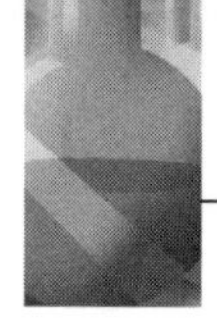

General

- Look at the marks available — make one good point per mark.
- Look at the number of lines available — this gives some idea of the length of answer required. Handwriting varies in size, but if you have written two words and there are three lines, assume you have not written enough to score full marks.
- Don't 'hedge your bets' — if you give two alternative answers, you will not get the marks unless both answers are correct. For example, if the answer is 0.04% and you write '± 0.25 or 0.04%' you will fail to score.
- Read the question — don't answer a question that you have invented. Markers have kind hearts and are genuinely sorry when they cannot award marks for an answer containing good chemistry that is not relevant to the question.

Command words in questions

A lot of care is taken in choosing which command words to use, so note their meanings carefully:

- **State, write down, give, name** — short answers only are required.
- **Describe** — an accurate account of the main points is required, without explanation.
- **Explain** — chemical reasons for the statement given are required.
- **Suggest** — you are not expected to know the answer but should be able to work it out from what you do know.
- **Give reason(s)** — requires you to explain why you chose to answer as you did (if 'reasons' in the plural is stated, judge the number of reasons required from the number of marks).

Avoid vague answers

Sometimes it is clear that the candidate knows quite a lot about the topic but his or her answer is not focused. Avoid the following words:

- 'It' (e.g. 'it is bigger') — give the name of whatever you are describing, otherwise it may not be clear to which object you are referring.
- 'Harmful' — if you mean 'toxic' or 'poisonous', say so.

Be careful with the names of chemical particles. Think twice whenever you write 'particle', 'atom', 'molecule' or 'ion' and check that you are using the correct term.

If in doubt, write something

Try to avoid leaving gaps. Make an attempt at every answer. If you're not sure, write something that seems to be sensible chemistry. Some questions have a number of possible answers — the only answer that definitely fails to score a mark is a blank space.

Calculations

It is easy to make mistakes, especially under the pressure of a task. So, set out the steps in your calculations clearly. Then, if you make a mistake but the marker can see what you are doing, you will still get most of the marks. Your teacher will mark calculations using a system called 'error carried forward' whereby, once an error has been made, the rest of the calculation scores marks if the method is correct from then on.

When you write down your numerical answer, check **units, sign** and **significant figures** (see p. 16).

Skill IV Observation

Here you are given a task sheet with specific practical instructions that tell you to carry out certain operations and write down your results. The results will be descriptions of what you observe. You are expected to be accurate and detailed in what you write. The task will last about 1 hour.

See the notes on 'Making observations' on pp. 14–15.

Skill V Interpretation

Here you are given a theoretical task that involves interpreting and explaining some practical observations. This will involve giving the relevant chemical theory and writing equations.

You will be given about 1 hour to do the task, although you may not need all this time.

If your teacher tells you the area of chemical theory that is being tested in the task, revise this using your own notes and also books, such as the student unit guides for Units F331 and F332, published by Philip Allan Updates.

You must be aware of the points about examination technique made in the section on Skill III (pp. 43–44).

The interpretation exercise may follow on from a Skill IV task that you have carried out recently.

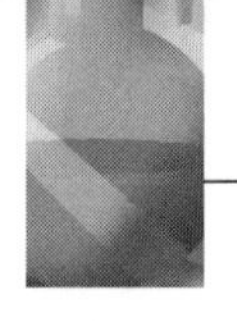

F336: The A2 individual investigation

The investigation gives you a glimpse of what chemical research is like. Remember the following important points:

- It is worth as many marks as Unit F334: Chemistry of Materials.
- It is your chance to do some work that you have devised, rather than just following instructions from an activity sheet.
- You need to plan carefully before you start.
- You need to spend as much time as you are allowed on practical work.
- You should keep it 'written up' as you go along.

Choosing an investigation

Your teacher will probably give you a lot of advice on choosing your investigation and you should take this advice. Your teacher knows the type of investigation that would suit your style and ability and also how different investigations fit with the resources and space provided by your school or college.

The advice below is thus general, but may be useful in helping you choose the most suitable investigation for you.

- Make sure that it is of A2 standard, i.e. based on A2 theory and of the level of the more demanding practical activities. Topics that could be investigated by GCSE candidates are not a good idea (an example is 'kettle descalers', although, as with any title, some people could make a suitable investigation from this).
- Make sure that it is essentially a chemistry project, not physics or biology. Check that the theory starts firmly from within your course.
- Make sure that your investigation includes some measurements. The marking points do cover qualitative investigations, but you should aim to measure something in order, for example, to compare preparative methods.
- Make sure that you cover enough ground to represent work taking place over 4 weeks. There is more advice on this below.

Where do I start?

A good place to start is with one of the activities that you have carried out. Then you have an initial method that you know works. Examples are shown in the table below, with examples of a useful follow-up and a poor follow-up.

Experiment	Useful follow-up	Poor follow-up
An aspirin assay	What happens when aspirin is treated in various ways?	How pure are samples of shop-bought aspirin?
Taking nylon apart (recrystallisation of hexanedioic acid)	Effect of varying recrystallisation methods on purity	Hydrolysing various types of nylon
Using the iodine clock method to find the order of a reaction	Going on to vary temperature and catalysts	Repeating the activity several times without extending it
Iodine/propanone reaction (methods of following reactions)	Measuring orders of reaction of reagents other than iodine; varying the temperature	Repeating the activity without extending it
How much copper is there in brass?	Use other methods of measuring copper(II) concentration and compare uncertainties and accuracy	How much copper is there in coins, drawing pins etc.?

You should discuss your ideas with your teacher at an early stage.

Your teacher may give you a starter sheet that gives you a jumping-off point for a title you have chosen.

The following points arise from the above ideas:

- You should design experiments that extend the activity and vary other factors. You should certainly investigate questions to which you do not *know* the answer and, if possible, investigate questions to which you can't look up the answer.
- You should not just keep repeating the activity 'trying to get more precise results'.
- You should *not* carry out the same test on lots of different samples (e.g. of aspirin, nylon or copper alloys) as the conclusions you can draw from such experiments are trivial — for example, 'this one contains more than that one'.
- You should not do the same investigation as anyone else in your class. Even if you start with the same activity as a 'jumping-off point' you are bound to vary your approach from there if you do not collude with them. Your teacher will guide you on this.
- Write the (provisional) aims of your investigation at an early stage. Examples of investigations that look promising are:
  - Investigating and comparing the conditions under which aspirin hydrolyses (followed by the conditions you are proposing to use).
  - How does the concentration of an Fe^{2+} catalyst affect the activation enthalpy of the peroxodisulfate/iodide reaction?
- Examples of investigations that do *not* look promising include:
  - Can I prepare a sample of aspirin by this method?
  - What is the enthalpy change of combustion of ethanol?
  - Which orange drink is the 'best buy' in terms of vitamin C content?

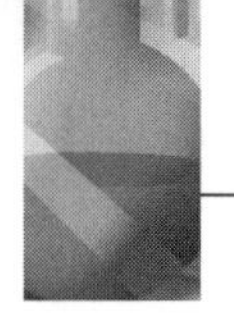

You can see that the conclusions from the first group will be at A2 whereas the conclusions from the second group will be short and/or relatively elementary.

There are many other useful suggestions on pp. 35 and 36 of the *OCR Practical Skills Handbook*, which can be found at:

www.ocr.org.uk/download/sm/ocr_32334_sm_gce_pract_skills_hb.pdf

Another useful table is at:

www.york.ac.uk/org/seg/salters/chemistry/investigation/invtable.html

Project Pages from past copies of *Chemistry Review* can be found at:

www.york.ac.uk/chemistry/schools/chemrev/projects/

Some instructions for carrying out practicals can be found at the Nuffield practical chemistry website:

www.practicalchemistry.org/experiments/advanced/category.html

A lot of useful information about investigations can be found at the Nuffield Re:act website, a student forum. The link below goes straight to the investigations section:

www.chemistry-react.org/go/Topic/Default_4.html

Other ideas include:

- There are several ways of measuring, for example, the concentration of a certain substance or the purity of a compound. Which is the most precise method and which is the most accurate? (See p. 22.)
- There are several ways of preparing compound X. Which gives the best yield and the purest product? (See 'Aspirin investigations' below.)
- Carry out a synthesis of Y. There are various ways of determining the purity. Evaluate these against the synthesised sample of Y and some pure Y.

Question

(28) You are discussing choices of investigation with your friends. How would you advise a friend who said:

(a) I am going to investigate how the viscosity of liquid alkanes varies with temperature. I will drop ball bearings into the alkanes and measure the time. There is lots of fascinating theory about viscosity that I can put in.

(b) I want to repeat an activity we did in class. I want to do all the experiments lots of times to see how accurate I can get them.

(c) I will measure the orders for my chosen reaction, and then go on to look at how the rate varies with temperature and catalysts.

(d) I will look at the colours of copper complexes.

(e) I will synthesise a compound in two ways. I will compare the percentage yield of my products and also their purity using three different methods.

(f) I will compare the colours in Smarties using paper chromatography.

(g) I will measure the amounts of vitamin C in orange drinks I buy to see if they agree with the data on the label.

(h) I will compare two methods of measuring the vitamin C concentration, using a known solution. I will then use my preferred method to investigate how much vitamin C is lost in chopping and boiling cabbage, investigating the cabbage and the water in which it is cooked.

Kinetics investigations

These are very popular, although you should not feel that you have to do one.

There are many 'starter sheets' available, either as activities or in the above list of websites.

It is a good idea to start by measuring the order of reaction with respect to several reagents (which is probably what the starter sheet says). When you have done this and gained familiarity with the method, consider varying the temperature and measuring the activation enthalpy (see p. 69) or using or varying the catalyst/inhibitor. If you decide on the latter, you should consider such questions as:

- If Fe^{2+} is a catalyst, is Fe^{3+} also a catalyst? Do other transition metal ions catalyse this reaction?
- Does the concentration of the catalyst affect the reaction rate?
- If an ion or a compound is an inhibitor, how dilute must it be before it has no effect?

Aspirin investigations

These investigations are popular but sometimes fail to score good marks.

A typical title that is somewhat suspect is 'How pure is the aspirin that I make and how does it compare with bought aspirin samples?' First, shop-bought aspirin is bound to have the purity stated on the packet, otherwise the firm selling it would be subject to heavy fines. Second, the methods of determining purity are more complicated than they appear:

- **Titrations with alkali** (as in 'An aspirin assay'). The issue here is that the main impurity in laboratory-made aspirin is salicylic acid, which also reacts with the alkali. There is a ratio method of solving this, but it is complicated.
- **Colorimetry** This involves hydrolysing the aspirin and measuring the concentration of the iron(III) complex that forms with the salicylic acid produced. However, this does not work if the sample is contaminated with salicylic acid to start with. Here, colorimetry can be used to measure the concentration of the *impurity* without hydrolysing first (see p. 36 for more on colorimetry).
- **Melting point** This indicates purity, but it is not possible to relate it to a percentage.
- **Thin-layer chromatography** This shows whether any other substance is present, it does not give percentage purity.

A better approach would be to investigate 'How can mixtures of aspirin and its hydrolysis product, salicylic acid, be analysed?' and use that to test either the rate of hydrolysis of aspirin under various conditions or how well the recrystallisation method works.

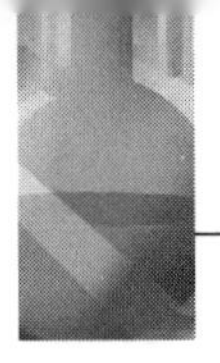

The route through your investigation

Stage	Action
Planning — choice	Choose as above and discuss with your teacher
Planning — research	Think through your practical method in detail Look up relevant theory Keep a note of references used Write a risk assessment Discuss with your teacher
Planning — writing up	Before you start you must write up a draft of what you propose to do, including practical methods, supporting theory, risk assessment and references Hand in your draft plan to your teacher before you start your investigation Your teacher will also want a list of apparatus and chemicals required
Doing (and reflecting on) experiments	Record the observations and measurements you make When you have finished practical work, hand these results (or a copy) to your teacher At this stage, hand in your finished planning section
Finishing off	Analyse and interpret your observations and measurements Evaluate your investigation Draw conclusions Hand this section to your teacher with a full copy of your results

Planning your investigation

Careful and thorough planning is essential if you are to make the best use of the practical time available to you.

Having decided on a topic, you need to look up or work out the practical method in some detail.

Your teacher *may* allow you to do a preliminary experiment before you submit your plan, provided you give full practical details and a risk assessment. This will enable you to try out the experiment on a 'starter sheet'.

You must then plan your experiments in detail and write risk assessments. There will be changes as you proceed and you discover what works and what does not. If you do new experiments you must, if necessary, submit extra risk assessments. Write out your methods in detail. You must also write up the background theory to your investigation and give all the references you have used.

Before you start, you must hand this draft plan in and get it *authenticated* by your teacher. Your teacher *cannot* allow you to start your investigation until you have done this. Authentication ensures that candidates have not copied their investigation reports from the internet or from someone else.

It is realised that your plan may evolve as the investigation proceeds, but it will not change completely. Consult your teacher if you want to make big changes to your plan.

For more advice on how to write up your plan, see skill areas A–C below.

Skill areas

Your investigation is marked in eight skill areas.

On your plan (the final version):

- chemical ideas
- methods
- communication

On your results:

- observations and measurements

On your final write-up:

- analysis and interpretation
- evaluation

Overall:

- manipulation
- demand

Each of these areas is now considered, with advice on how to maximise your marks.

Skill area A: Chemical ideas

This mark is based on the part of your plan in which you write about the theoretical background to your investigation.

You should be sure that the relevant background theory is covered in the correct depth for A2. For example, in a kinetics experiment, you should give the theory of rate equations and order of reaction (related to your experiment) and also the Arrhenius theory if you are using this to measure the activation enthalpy (see p. 69). You should give relevant theory of catalysis if appropriate. (Be prepared to look up theory outside the scope of the A2 course.) Then you should give the equation for the reaction you are studying and the theory of the method you are going to use, indicating which graphs you are going to plot and how you are going to calculate the results.

The theory must be *relevant* to what you actually do. Do not write about, for example, colorimetry if you are not going to use it. However, if you are using colorimetry, make sure that you describe it fully and include details of calibration curves. If your investigation changes from your original plan, you may have to re-visit these theory areas to make sure that they are all still relevant and that you have not left anything out.

Skill area B: Methods

Make sure that you describe clearly the *aims* of your investigation. Your draft plan should contain your initial aims. These may change somewhat as you move through the investigation, so be sure to re-visit your aims at the end to ensure they reflect what you actually did. You should put your aims at the beginning of your investigation, under the title.

Describe the method you are going to use in full, in the same detail as it is described in an activity sheet.

Give details of the reagents you are going to use. You should indicate how you will obtain solutions of particular concentrations. As a general rule, you should make up some of these solutions, giving details of the amounts weighed etc. Other solutions may be supplied.

Give details of the apparatus you will use and how you intend to use it. It is important, if you will be measuring a volume, for example, to consider which piece of measuring equipment is suitable and then to be sure to name it in your account.

Think about fine detail in your measurements. For example, if you will be measuring gas volumes against time in a rate experiment, record the times taken for increasing volumes to be produced (e.g. 5, 10, 15 cm^3), rather than just the time for a much larger volume (e.g. 20 cm^3).

Think about repetitions — how many times should you repeat an experiment? This depends on the consistency of the first two runs (see p. 55 for more detail).

You are so close to your experiments that it is easy for you to leave out details or even whole stages. Read your method through critically to check for omissions.

However, try to avoid a great deal of repetition. 'I repeated the experiment keeping the concentrations the same but varying the temperature. I varied the temperature by...' is better than giving all the experimental details again. The use of tables to show how you intend to change the variables is recommended.

Skill area C: Communication

This concerns three areas:

- risk assessment
- references
- clarity, vocabulary and quality of written communication

Risk assessments

Risk assessments must cover all the reagents you use, as well as any hazardous processes and any hazardous products.

Your teacher will give you a set of references in which you can look up the chemicals you are using. These could be 'Hazcards'.

Risk assessments must indicate the hazard and the precautions that need to be taken. They must be relevant to the concentrations being used — a common error is to give the risks for concentrated sulfuric acid when only dilute acid is being used. Neither should you give the hazards of a solid when you are using a solution of that substance. Do not copy out the whole Hazcard.

Examples of good risk assessments

Some examples of good risk assessment are given in the table below. They are not necessarily from the same investigation.

Substance	Details	Risks	Precautions
Copper(II) sulfate solution	2.0 mol dm^{-3} solution	Harmful if swallowed and to eyes and skin Dangerous to aquatic organisms	If solution is swallowed or gets into the eyes report immediately to teacher; wash hands thoroughly after use; dilute with at least five times as much water before pouring down sink
Potassium bromate(V)	Solid and 0.0167 mol dm^{-3} solution	Both toxic, may cause cancer	Wear gloves when handling both (especially solid); if swallowed report immediately to teacher; dilute with at least three times as much water before pouring down sink
Butan-1-ol	Liquid	Flammable; harmful if swallowed; irritating to eyes and skin; harmful vapor; absorbed through skin	Use in a fume cupboard; no flames close by; wear gloves
Sulfur dioxide	Made as a result of acids reacting with sulfate(IV) salts	Toxic gas	Use fume cupboard
Sodium hyposulfite solution	0.1 mol dm^{-3}	Low hazard	Normal laboratory safety precautions

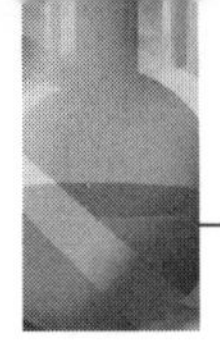

Question

(29) Criticise the following poor risk assessments:

(a) I am using 0.2 mol dm^{-3} sulfuric acid. I will wear goggles and gloves as this is a highly corrosive liquid.

(b) In an experiment where magnesium is being reacted with dilute acids: 'Magnesium is a dangerous solid that explodes with silver nitrate and sulfur.'

(c) I will take care since a toxic gas is formed in this experiment.

(d) This reagent is harmful so I shall wear a lab coat and safety glasses.

References

All scientific papers quote references to websites and books that have been used. Your investigation must do the same.

When you are writing your plan, make a note of each website and book that you use.

Make a note in the text each time you use a reference, e.g. 'The equation for the reaction is shown below (1)'. The reference, (1), gives the detail of the reference where you looked up the equation.

List your references at the end of your plan, in order of reference number. For websites give the URL, the date you accessed it and a brief statement of its contents (since web addresses do not always indicate this). For books, give the title, the publisher, the edition and the author, then the page reference and a brief statement of what you find there. For example:

(1) www.salts.com (accessed dd/mm/yy) Hydrolysis of salts

(2) *Salters Chemical Ideas*, Heinemann, 3rd edn (Otter & Stephenson ed.), p. 23, Radioactive tracers

Aim for several different websites (you may refer to the same site more than once, but aim for a total of five different sites).

Aim for several different sources — *at least* eight references in all, including websites.

You may refer to the same book more than once, but aim for several different ones in all.

Question

(30) A student gives the following list of references to his or her investigation:

www.aspirin.co.uk

A big red chemistry book in the library

Salters Chemical Storylines, The Atmosphere

***Salters Chemical Ideas*, p. 55**

How would you advise the student to do better?

Clarity, vocabulary, quality of written communication

As well as looking at your risk assessment and references, the skill C mark for communication includes the communication skills of clarity, vocabulary and 'quality of written communication' (QWC). These are assessed on your final plan.

Make sure that your report is clear and lucid and organised logically. Read it through at the end to check this. The report will be word-processed, so you can move bits of text around to make it more logical, or you can add to sections to make it clearer.

Use specialist terms whenever possible — for example, **rate of reaction** rather than speed of reaction and **collisions** of molecules, rather than molecules hitting.

Make sure that your spelling is accurate throughout, particularly the technical terms. Use the spell-check, but be careful not to click on the suggested word without checking that it is correct. This can cause amazing errors — for example, 'Arrhenius' has the suggestion 'arsenics' and 'pipetting' has 'pupating'.

Check that the grammar and punctuation are accurate.

Skill area D: Observations and measurements

Reread the section on 'Reading instruments' on pp. 9–11. When carrying out your investigation make sure that you are following the principles given there. If a variety of instruments are available for making a measurement (e.g. burette or measuring cylinder for volume, 0.1°C or 1°C thermometer), make sure that you use the one appropriate for the measurement you need to take, and record why in your practical method.

Reread the section on 'Recording data' on p. 11. Record your data in tables, with the correct number of decimal places and units. Give each table a title.

Relate the tables you draw up to those you have proposed in your plan.

Record your results in a notebook, rather than on loose pieces of paper, which may get lost.

You have to hand in your results as soon as you have finished your practical work. These need not be 'polished', but they will be your true results. Your teacher is then able to check that candidates have not adjusted their results when writing up, or invented more results. Even if you would not be tempted to do either of these things, it is important to you that no-one else is doing it.

Your teacher will give you your results back so that you can write the rest of your report. You can type the results into tables in the report, but ensure that no discrepancies creep in.

Look at your results critically at frequent intervals:

- Think about the number of readings (e.g. number of different concentrations, number of different temperatures). A minimum of five readings is needed to plot a decent graph.
- Think about repetitions — if the results of two runs are consistent, then one more run will be ample. You may need to repeat runs where you get big differences, and consider why the differences are large.

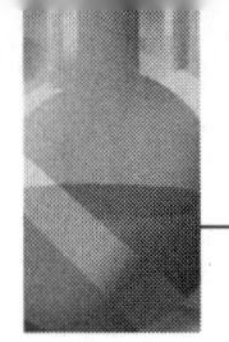

- Think about uncertainties. If you get small titres (smaller than $10\,cm^3$ when you are titrating $25\,cm^3$ in the flask), you need to vary the concentration of one of the reagents so that you get a larger titre, with a smaller uncertainty. If the times you measure for a colour change are very short, you should adjust the concentrations until the times are longer, i.e. the reaction is slower.

If you are making observations, reread the section on 'Making observations' on pp. 14–15. It is usually best to record your observations in a table, showing the test and its result. If appropriate, include the conclusion from the test, or a comment on the reliability and validity of the observations.

Test	Observation	Comments/Conclusion
Add $0.05\,mol\,dm^{-3}$ silver nitrate solution to a solution of A in dilute nitric acid	Thick white precipitate (repeated three times)	Reliable and valid conclusion that A is a chloride
Add $0.05\,mol\,dm^{-3}$ barium chloride solution to a solution of A in dilute nitric acid	Faint white precipitate	
Repeat above with $1.0\,mol\,dm^{-3}$ barium chloride solution	Faint white precipitate	Reasonably reliable evidence that A is *not* a sulfate

Skill area E: Analysis and interpretation

Calculations

Reread the section on calculations (pp. 15–18) and make sure that you have covered the points given there.

It is tricky to present calculations well in a word-processed document and you will have to work hard at this. If possible, use Equation Editor. Make sure your calculations are well laid out, with words to explain what you are doing.

Carry out calculations and plot graphs while you are taking results, so that you can investigate any strange things that happen.

Graphs

Reread the information about graphs on pp. 12–14.

Wherever possible, present your results as graphs. For more detail on rates of reaction graphs, see pp. 65–69.

Plot some graphs by hand, especially where you need to read off results accurately or a complicated curve has to be drawn.

If you use a graph-plotting package, be sure you understand how to use it properly. Otherwise plot by hand — there are no marks for IT skills.

Make sure that the graph is big enough, has all labels, shows the origin if necessary, has a grid that enables values to be read accurately and does not have meaningless information included, such as 'series 1'.

It is usually best to draw lines of best fit by hand, even if you have computerised the graph.

Make sure that the tables of results are as close as possible to the graphs in your report and that it is made clear on each graph which table is being plotted.

Do not place all your graphs together in one part of the report or at the end.

Outcomes and conclusions

For observations, it might be useful to record your conclusions and comments from individual tests etc. in the table of results.

For calculations and graphs, give the conclusions clearly after the calculation or on the graph. For example, 'The percentage yield of this reaction is 15 ± 1%' (the uncertainty will come from calculations done in your evaluation) or 'This graph shows a straight line through the origin (within the limits of uncertainty shown by the error bars) and thus the reaction is first order with respect to...'

Give an overall conclusion at the end. For example, 'My investigation showed that, of all the methods I used to analyse the concentration of W in solution, method X was the most precise (least variation between the repeats) but method Y was the most accurate (the average was nearest to the known value)'.

Make sure that you refer to your background theory (from the plan) to justify your calculations, outcomes and conclusions. Quote the relevant parts of the theory again, rather than simply referring back to your plan.

Skill area F: Evaluation

This is one of the most difficult skill areas and needs a lot of attention. Your work will be assessed in the four categories given below.

Ideally, you should consider this section while you are obtaining your results. Then, if there is a large uncertainty in a particular measurement, you may be able to improve on it by, for example, changing the concentrations of solutions or using a more precise measuring device. You should comment on this in your evaluation of 'Choice of materials, equipment and procedures'.

Limitations of procedures

You need to aim for about four relevant limitations and treat them in detail. These are discussed under 'Systematic errors' on pp. 22–24.

A summary of some possible limitations to consider follows. However, you should be aware that not all will be relevant to your experiment and also that there will be other, specific limitations that you should mention. Limitations include:

- human error in reading a timer
- judging a difficult end point
- taking a fluctuating reading
- heat losses
- multiple operations (mixing solutions and starting timer)

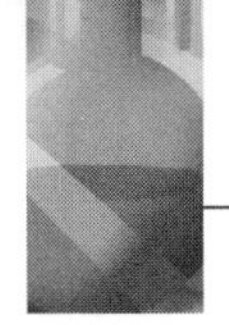

- having to use different batches of solution (provided you have kept a note of where different batches were used and can show that this has an effect)
- changing background temperature between sessions (with details, if possible)

Comments on observations

This will apply if you do any qualitative work. Ensure that you have commented on the reliability and validity of all observations (see pp. 25 and 56).

Percentage uncertainties

Reread pp. 19–21.

Work out percentage uncertainites for *all* types of measurement that you make. Types of measurement are, for example, burette readings and temperature readings. Work out the uncertainty of a typical (average) value.

It is easy to overlook some, for example:

- measurements of time (work this out, even if you think that human error is more important)
- measurements made when making up a solution — balance and volumetric flask

Choice of materials, equipment and procedures

You should aim for *at least* three different comments.

Examples are given below, but note that not all will be relevant to your investigation and there will be others that are:

- choice of thermometer (1°C or 0.1°C) to fit other uncertainties
- reduction of overall uncertainty by changing the piece of apparatus with greatest uncertainty
- ways of reducing the limitations you have discussed
- whether systematic error or uncertainties have the greater effect on your answer (see pp. 22–24)
- comments on repetitions
- comments on the techniques used for making up solutions and carrying out titrations

It is a good idea to tabulate these comments in two columns, with the headings 'choice' and 'reason'.

Skill area G: Manipulation

Your teacher will assess you by observation while you are carrying out practical work.

The three categories for assessment are:

- working safely
- manipulative skills
- organisation

Working safely

- Always work to your highest standards.
- Be aware of the hazards you describe in your risk assessments.
- Report any safety problems to your teacher immediately.

Manipulative skills

- Do everything as carefully as possible, using the skills you have learned.
- Don't rush things or try to 'cut corners'.
- Try to resolve problems without help (unless there are safety implications). However, you should discuss things with your teacher if you feel that you are getting stuck.

Organisation

- Make sure your practical place is always well-organised and clean.
- Write down all your results in a notebook as you obtain them.

Skill area H: Demand

This is a different kind of assessment, because it assesses the nature of your investigation topic as well as your approach to the investigation.

It is designed to recognise that some investigation topics are harder than others — they have 'greater demand'.

Your teacher will help you to choose the most demanding topic of which you are capable. If you choose one that is too difficult for you, you will probably get lower marks in many of the other assessment areas, even if you get a slightly better mark for demand.

The ways in which you can help yourself are to ensure that you:

- go much further than the 'starter sheet' you use
- keep thinking of ways of developing your investigation throughout the time you are given for practical work
- try to devise developing practical methods for yourself (but write risk assessments and get them checked by your teacher)
- consult your teacher regularly about what you have done and how you might proceed

Question

(31) You are discussing your investigations with fellow students. They make the following statements. Which of these statements might lead to a high mark for demand?

(a) I measured the order of reaction for the three reagents.

(b) I plotted a graph of rate of reaction against temperature.

(c) I measured the rate of reaction at different temperatures and worked out the activation enthalpy.

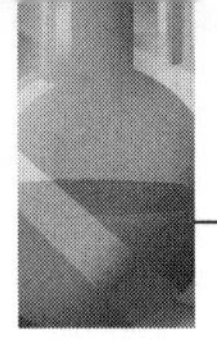

(d) I varied the catalyst and worked out the activation enthalpy for different catalysts.

(e) Having measured the activation enthalpy, I tried out the effect of various cations and anions on the rate of reaction.

(f) In a book in the library, I found ways of making transition metals in their highest oxidation states. I tried some of these and devised ways of proving that I had made what I set out to make.

(g) I investigated how much aspirin there was in different tablets using a sodium hydroxide titration, to identify which was the 'best buy'.

(h) I devised methods resembling storing aspirin under different conditions and treated samples of aspirin according to these methods. I then tried out ways of measuring the purity of aspirin and used the best ones on my treated samples.

Assessment of your investigation

You have to hand in your investigation in stages.

Stage 1 Draft plan

The draft plan should contain:

- aims
- theory (including theory of experiments)
- methods for experiments
- indication of how experimental results will relate to aims
- risk assessment (very important)
- references

Your teacher will also want a list of the apparatus and chemicals you will need in order to be able to start.

Your teacher will 'authenticate' your draft plan. This is to assure everyone that it is your work and that you have had only the help allowed by the rules. You will then be given your draft plan (or a copy of it) back. Your teacher will discuss the plan with you.

Stage 2 Results

As soon as the time for practical work is over, your teacher will ask you for your results.

Your teacher will decide the format required, but it may well be photocopies of pages from your notebook.

Your teacher will 'authenticate' the results, to show that they are yours. (You will have been observed while carrying out the experiments.)

You may change the presentation of the results from that in your notebook, but you must not alter results or add to them.

Stage 3 The whole investigation report

Use the following as a checklist for the content of your report.

Plan

This will be collected soon after you finish the practical work. It will have evolved from your draft plan. If you feel that it has changed a great deal, then consult your teacher.

Your plan should contain:

- aims — modified, if necessary, to reflect what you actually did
- theory — both background theory and theory of the experiments and calculations you carried out. Make sure that this theory is comprehensive, accurate and detailed (A2 level) and relevant to what you finally did.
- experimental procedures described in full, including the fine detail — for example, concentrations stated to an appropriate number of significant figures
- risk assessment — detailed and relevant (see pp. 52–53)
- technical terms — used correctly and spelt correctly
- references — at least eight, detailed and linked to the text (see p. 54)

The whole report should be readable and logical, with correct spelling, punctuation and grammar.

Results

Make sure that all results are arranged neatly in tables with clear titles and headings (observations *and* measurements).

Make sure that units and significant figures are correct.

Analysis and interpretation

- All calculations should be explained clearly and the answer stated clearly.
- All graphs should be well-drawn with a title and labelled axes.
- All observations should have comments on reliability and validity (see pp. 25 and 56).
- The outcomes of separate experiments, as well as the overall conclusions, should be stated clearly.

Evaluation

Reread the advice on pp. 57–58.

Make sure that:

- limitations of the experimental procedures (at least four) are given
- percentage uncertainties of *all* types of measurement are calculated
- validity and reliability of *all* observations are given (see pp. 25 and 56)
- choices of equipment, materials and procedures are justified (at least three)

Your teacher will 'authenticate' the whole report and sign a form to say that it is your work and that any help you had was within the rules.

Appendix

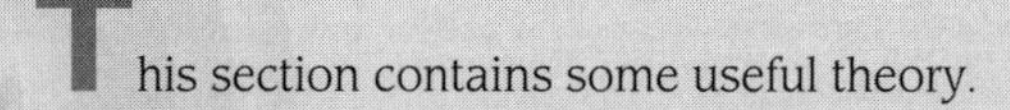

This section contains some useful theory.

- Reaction rate graphs — including theory of rate equations, rate constants and measuring orders of reaction.
- The Arrhenius equation — how to plot a graph to measure the activation enthalpy.
- The Nernst equation — the variation of E_{cell} with concentration.

Useful theory

Reaction-rate graphs

The **rate of reaction** at a given moment is defined as the change in concentration divided by the time taken for the change.

Rate equation and rate constant

The **rate equation** for a reaction A + B → products is:

$$\text{rate} = k[A]^a[B]^b$$

where k is the **rate constant**, square brackets represent concentrations in $mol\,dm^{-3}$ and a and b are the **orders of reaction** with respect to A and B. (The overall order of reaction is $a + b$.)

Units of the rate constant

The units of rate are $mol\,dm^{-3}\,s^{-1}$.

Thus for an overall first-order reaction:

$$k = \text{rate}/[\text{reagent}]$$

units of $k = mol\,dm^{-3}\,s^{-1}/mol\,dm^{-3} = \mathbf{s^{-1}}$

For a second-order reaction:

$$k = \text{rate}/[\text{reagent}]^2$$

units $= mol\,dm^{-3}\,s^{-1}/mol^2\,dm^{-6} = \mathbf{mol^{-1}\,dm^3\,s^{-1}}$

Measuring order of reaction

Order of reaction has nothing to do with the overall balanced chemical equation for the reaction because this usually represents a series of steps. Order of reaction must be measured by experiment.

Method 1

This involves measuring the time for a small proportion of the reaction to occur.

For example, suppose that three reagents A, B and C react. Sets of experiments are carried out in which the concentrations of B and C are kept constant and the concentration of A is varied.

The volume is kept constant in each experiment, so that the volume of each reagent is proportional to its concentration.

An example of a suitable table is shown on p. 66.

- The experiment is repeated varying B (keeping A and C constant) and then varying C (keeping A and B constant).
- A graph is drawn of 1/time (proportional to rate) on the y-axis against volume of A (proportional to concentration) on the x-axis.

Tube	A/cm^3	B/cm^3	C/cm^3	Water/ cm^3	Time 1 /s	Time 2 /s	Time 3 /s	Average time/s	1/time /s^{-1}
1	1.0	5.0	5.0	4.0					
2	2.0	5.0	5.0	3.0					
3	3.0	5.0	5.0	2.0					
4	4.0	5.0	5.0	1.0					
5	5.0	5.0	5.0	0.0					

- If the result is a straight line through the origin, then the reaction is **first order with respect to A.**
- If the result is a curve, the reaction is probably second order. Check this by plotting the rate against the square of the concentration. The reaction is **second order** if this graph is a straight line through the origin. Alternatively, you could plot log (rate) against log (concentration). In this case, the gradient gives the order.
- If the rate remains constant when the concentration changes (a horizontal line), the reaction is **zero order**.

Graphs for orders of reaction are shown in Figure 16.

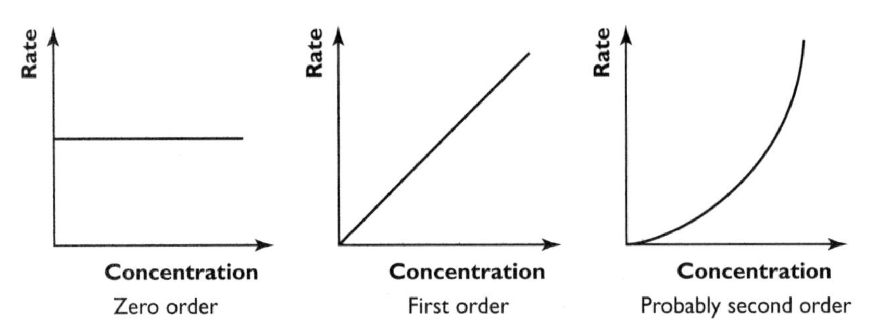

Figure 16 Rate against concentration for various orders of reaction

In order to determine the rate constant, k, from these data:

- Write down the rate equation when you know all the orders, e.g. rate = $k[A][B][C]^2$.
- Work out the rate in mol dm^{-3} s^{-1} (work out the relationship between 'the amount of reagent formed or used when timing is stopped' and its concentration).
- Substitute values for rate and [A], [B] and [C] into the rate equation for several of your sets of data. Work out k and average the values.

Worked example

The table contains the results of experiments to measure the rate of a reaction (which has three reactants) in terms of the time taken for a certain amount of iodine to form. 2.0 cm^3 of 0.001 mol dm^{-3} sodium thiosulfate solution were added to react with a specific amount of iodine formed.

Volume of 0.10 mol dm^{-3} A /cm^3 (±0.1)	Volume of 0.10 mol dm^{-3} B /cm^3	Volume of 0.10 mol dm^{-3} C /cm^3	Volume of water /cm^3	Volume of thiosulfate /cm^3	Time /s ±1	$\frac{1}{t}$ /s^{-1} [a]
1.0	1.0	1.0	5.0	2.0	205 (±0.5%)	0.00488 (±0.00002)
2.0	1.0	1.0	4.0	2.0	95 (±1%)	0.0105 (±0.0001)
3.0	1.0	1.0	3.0	2.0	67 (±1%)	0.0150 (±0.0002)
4.0	1.0	1.0	2.0	2.0	48 (±2%)	0.0208 (±0.0004)
5.0	1.0	1.0	1.0	2.0	37 (±3%)	0.0270 (± 0.0008)

[a]Uncertainty is same % as time — then converted to ±

The graph is plotted below with error bars. These are not essential in the individual investigation, but they do enable you to see whether the points all 'touch' the best fit line.

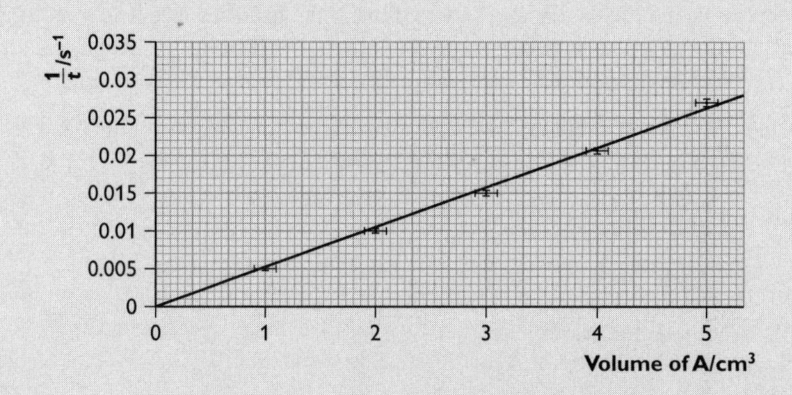

Figure 17 A graph of 1/t against volume

The graph shows that rate is proportional to concentration, within the limits of uncertainty.

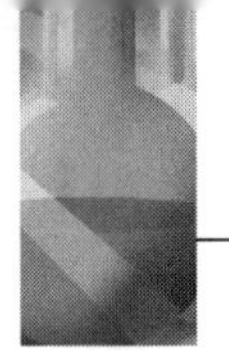

To work out k:

- Relate 1/time to rate:
  amount $Na_2S_2O_3 = 2.0 \times 0.0010/1000 = 2.0 \times 10^{-6}$ mol
  equation: $I_2 + 2Na_2S_2O_3 \rightarrow 2NaI + Na_2S_4O_6$
  So, amount of iodine produced = 1.0×10^{-6} mol in $10\,cm^3 = 1.0 \times 10^{-4}\,mol\,dm^{-3}$
  Values of $1/t$ must be multiplied by 1.0×10^{-4} to give the rate in $mol(I_2)\,dm^{-3}\,s^{-1}$
- $1.0\,cm^3$ of any of the reagents contributes $1.0 \times 0.10/10.0$ to the concentration $= 1.0 \times 10^{-2}$
- Assume rate equation (from your experiments) is:
  rate = $k[A][B][C]^2$
- Take a point that is exactly on the line (one of the most accurate), e.g. $2.0\,cm^3$ A:
  rate = $0.0105 \times 10^{-4}\,mol\,dm^{-3}\,s^{-1}$
  $k = 0.0105 \times 10^{-4} / ((2.0 \times 10^{-2}) \times (1.0 \times 10^{-2}) \times (1.0 \times 10^{-2})^2)$
  $= 0.0105 \times 10^{-4} / 2.0 \times 10^{-8}$
  So, $k = 53\,dm^9\,mol^{-3}\,s^{-1}$ (2 s.f.)

Method 2

This involves following the reaction over the course of its progress. The reaction is followed by either:

- measuring the concentration of a reactant or product against time *or*
- by measuring a property which is proportional to the concentration

One reagent is **limiting** (in smaller concentration than the others) and a graph is plotted of the concentration of this reactant against time. If the **half-life** (see below) is constant, the reaction is first order with respect to the limiting reagent. (If the graph is a straight line, it is zero order; if successive half-lives increase it is probably second order.)

For example, the graph in Figure 18 shows the variation of concentration of X with time.

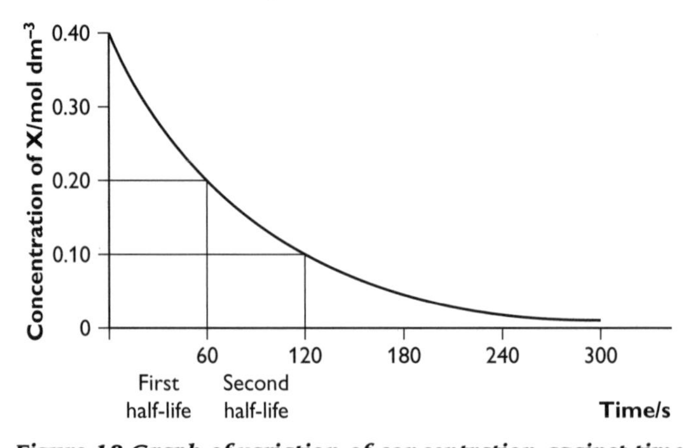

Figure 18 Graph of variation of concentration against time

The first half-life is the time taken for the concentration to fall from 0.4 to 0.2. The second half-life is the time taken for the concentration to fall from 0.2 to 0.1. They are both 60 seconds, so the reaction is first order with respect to X.

The gradient at various concentrations gives the rate at that concentration. You could measure several of these from the graph and then plot graphs of rate against concentration as in Method 1.

Arrhenius equation

The Arrhenius equation is not required for the theory papers. However, you will need it if you study the variation of rate of reaction with temperature.

The relationship between the rate constant for a reaction and the temperature is:

$$k = Ae^{(-E_a/RT)}$$

where E_a is the activation enthalpy, T is the temperature in Kelvin and R is a constant, know as the universal gas constant ($8.31\,J\,K^{-1}\,mol^{-1}$).

$e^{(-E_a/RT)}$ represents the proportion of molecules with energy greater than E_a.

A is constant for a particular reaction and is related to the proportion of molecules that collide in such a way that reaction is possible, due to their shape.

The mathematical constant 'e' may not be familiar to you if you no longer study maths. The following expression, which can be derived from the Arrhenius equation, might not look quite so frightening:

$$\ln k = \ln A - E_a/RT$$

This uses 'natural logarithms' which again might be a concern. However, all you need to do is to press the correct button on your calculator (marked 'ln', rather than 'lg' or 'log').

Again depending on your mathematical ability, you may recognise that this is the equation of a straight line if $\ln k$ is plotted against $1/T$.

If the concentrations of the reagents are kept constant when the temperature is varied, then k is proportional to the initial rate.

So, a graph of ln rate against $1/T$ has a gradient of $-E_a/R$ (gradient is the change in y/the change in x).

This is illustrated in Figure 19.

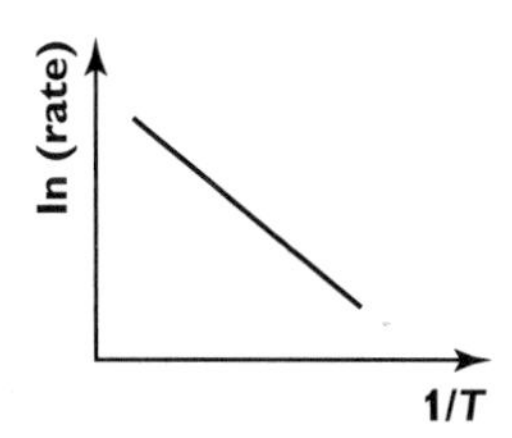

Figure 19 Arrhenius plot

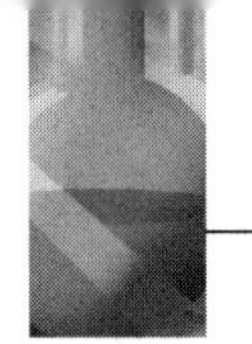

Worked example

Here are some data on the variation of rate against temperature for the reaction:

$2HI(g) \rightarrow H_2(g) + I_2(g)$

Plot a graph of ln rate against $1/T$ and find E_a.

Temperature/K	Rate	$\frac{10^3}{T}$ /K^{-1}	ln rate
559	0.0176	1.79	–4.04
649	42.9	1.54	+3.76
704	580	1.42	+6.36
781	19800	1.28	+9.89

The graph is shown in Figure 20.

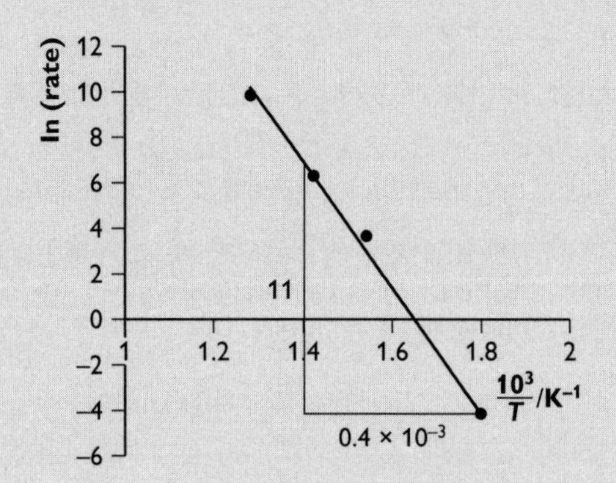

Figure 20 Graph of ln(rate) against 1/T

The gradient is $-11.0/0.4 \times 10^{-3} = -27\,500$

Thus, $E_a/R = 27\,500$, so $E_a = 27\,500 \times 8.31 = 230 \times 10^3\,\text{J mol}^{-1}$ or $+230\,\text{kJ mol}^{-1}$

Question

(32) The rate of a reaction varies with temperature as shown. Calculate a value for E_a.

T/K	Rate
278	1.5
298	41
308	200
323	1400

The Nernst equation

You will need to be aware of the Nernst equation if you are using electrical cells and measuring how the cell potential varies with concentration. It is not required for the written papers.

The equation for an electrode consisting of a metal dipping into its ions in solution is:

$$E = E^{\ominus} + (RT/zF) \times \ln[\text{ion}]$$

where R is the gas constant, T is the temperature in K, F is the Faraday constant and z is the number of positive charges on the metal ion, ln = 2.3 log.

The constants are not important to the variation of E with concentration and ln can be converted to log, giving:

$$E = E^{\ominus} + (0.059/z) \times \log[\text{ion}]$$

So, for a metal/metal ion electrode:

- when [ion] = 1 (standard conditions) $E = E^{\ominus}$
- when the ion concentration varies, E varies as shown in the graph in Figure 21.

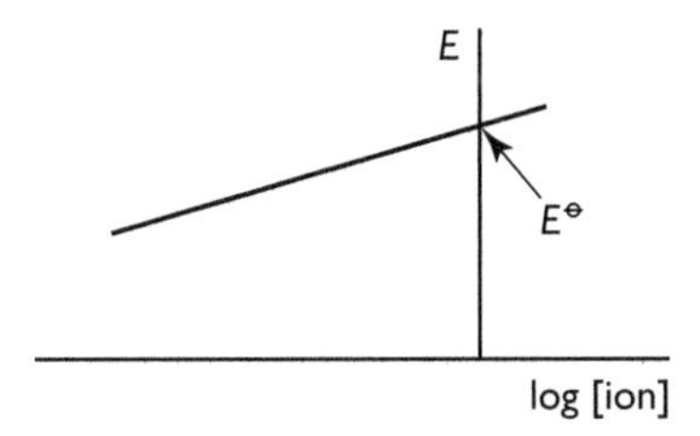

Figure 21 Nernst equation plot

- Notice that log [ion] is like pH. When the ion concentration changes by one power of ten, log [ion] changes by just *one* unit.
- The moral is: if you want to get significant changes in the electrode potential you measure, you must vary the concentration of the ion by powers of ten e.g. 1.0, 0.10, 0.010 mol dm^{-3}, not 1.0, 0.50, 0.25 mol dm^{-3}.

Answers

This section of the guide gives the answers to the questions that are asked throughout this guide. Make sure you attempt the question yourself before checking the answer here.

Answers

(1) **(a)** 46.35 cm^3 **(b)** 19.50 cm^3

(2) **(a)** 8.45 cm^3 **(b)** 32.5 cm^3 **(c)** 37.0 cm^3

(3) **(a)** 16.0°C **(b)** 0.22°C **(c)** –3.0°C

(4) Masses should be tabulated; second mass should be 0.030 g
Burette readings should be tabulated and 'first reading, second reading, volume' should be given for each, plus the units (cm^3)
30.0 and 45.3 should be 30.00 and 45.30

(5)

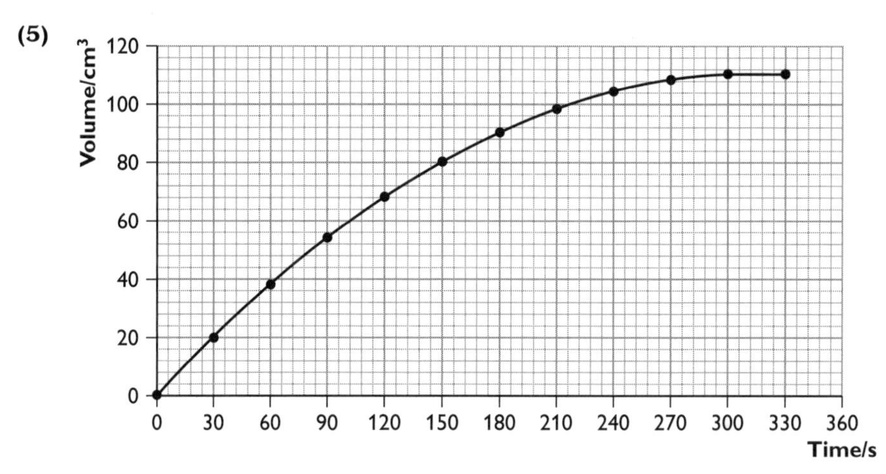

(6)

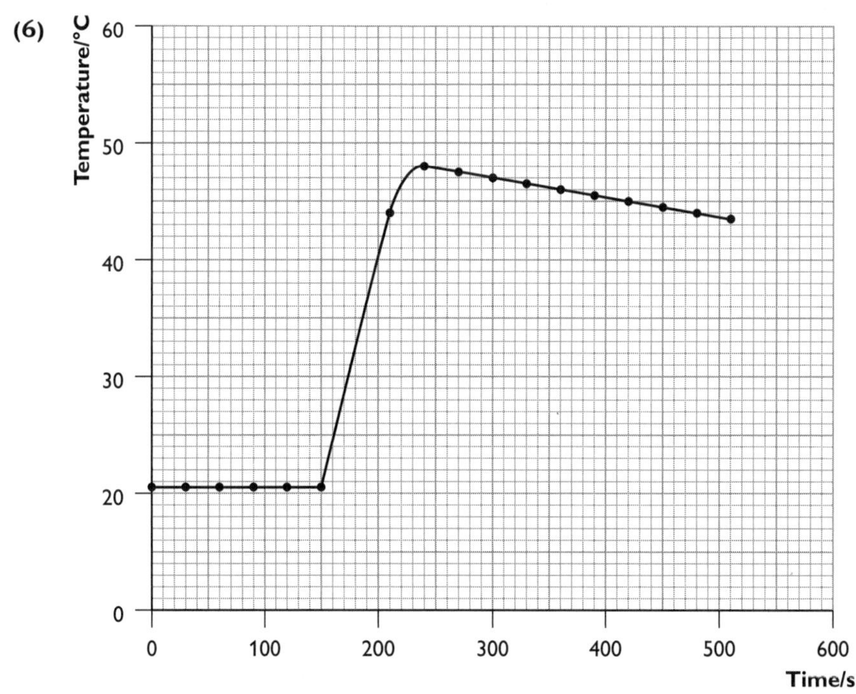

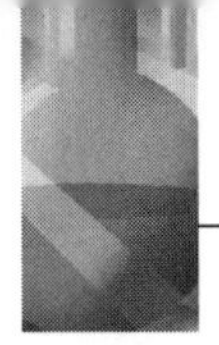

(7) **(a)** 0.31 (± 0.02) $cm^3 s^{-1}$
(b) Zero
(c) 0.41 (±0.02) $cm^3 s^{-1}$

(8) **(a)** The solution went yellow. Two layers were formed when the cyclohexane was added. The top (cyclohexane) layer was orange and the bottom one was yellow.
(b) A faint white precipitate was formed.
(c) On mixing, the solution went very dark red.

(9) **(a)** 2, 3, 2, 1, 5, 2 or 3 (If it were 2.5×10^2, it would be 2 s.f.)
(b) 15.47 (note: round up if the final figure is 5 or greater than 5), 15.5, 15
(c) 0.050 is 2 s.f., so the answer should be 0.0010 mol (or 1.0×10^{-3} mol)
(d) This is trickier because it depends on the data source for the M_r. If you use the Salters Data Sheet, A_r values are given to one decimal place. Hence the M_r value comes to 46.0 (though the value of the M_r can be looked up elsewhere to much greater precision). Thus, although the mass is to 4 s.f., the M_r is only to 3 s.f. Hence the answer is 0.100 mol (or 1.00×10^{-1} mol)

(10) **(a)** $Na_2CO_3 + 2HCl \rightarrow 2NaCl + CO_2 + H_2O$
(b) M_r of Na_2CO_3 = 106.0, so moles = 10.6/106.0 = 0.100 mol
moles of HCl = 100 × 1.0/1000 = 0.10 mol
0.1 mol Na_2CO_3 requires 0.2 mol HCl, so the Na_2CO_3 is in excess

In the following calculations, the moles of HCl (0.10) are used, since all the HCl is used up.

(c) From the equation, 0.10 mol HCl produces 0.050 mol CO_2
volume = 0.050 × 24 = 1.2 dm^3
(d) From the equation, 0.10 mol HCl produces 0.10 mol NaCl
M_r of NaCl = 58.5, so 5.9 g (2 s.f.) are produced.

(11) moles of Na_2CO_3 = 25.00 × 0.0200/1000 = 5.00×10^{-4} mol
equation: $Na_2CO_3 + 2HCl \rightarrow 2NaCl + H_2O + CO_2$
moles of HCl = 2 × 5.00 × 10^{-4} = 1.00×10^{-3} mol
concentration = 1.00×10^{-3} × 1000/27.15 = 0.0368 mol dm^{-3}

(12) moles of H_2SO_4 = 24.30 × 0.100/1000 = 0.00243 mol
equation: $2NaHCO_3 + H_2SO_4 \rightarrow Na_2SO_4 + 2CO_2 + H_2O$
moles of $NaHCO_3$ = 2 × 0.00243 = 0.00486 mol
concentration = 0.00486 × 1000/25.00 = 0.194 mol dm^{-3}

(13) amount of NaOH added = 24.65 × 0.100/1000 = 2.465×10^{-3} mol
amount of citric acid in 25.00 cm^3 = $2.465 \times 10^{-3}/3 = 8.22 \times 10^{-4}$ mol
amount of citric acid in 250 cm^3 = 8.22×10^{-3} mol
M_r of citric acid = 192.1
mass of pure citric acid in 250 cm^3 = 8.22×10^{-3} × 192.1 = 1.58 g
% = 1.58 × 100/5.00 = 31.6 %

(14) **(a)** $\pm 1\,cm^3$ 4%
(b) $\pm 0.5\,cm^3$ 2%
(c) $\pm 0.25\,cm^3$ 1%
(d) $\pm 0.05\,cm^3$ 0.2%
(e) $\pm 0.5°C$ 1.25%
(f) $\pm 0.05°C$ 0.125%
(g) $\pm 0.005\,g$ 0.033%
(h) $\pm 0.05\,mol\,dm^{-3}$ 1.7%

(15) Values are: concentration, $0.40 \pm 0.005\,mol\,dm^{-3}$ (1.25%); burette reading, 26.3 ± 0.1 (0.4%); pipette reading, $25.0 \pm 0.06\,cm^3$ (0.24%)
So the concentration contributes most.

(16) $0.59 \pm 0.01\,g$

(17) $0.01 \times 100/0.05 = 20\%$

(18) **(a)** A — the uncertainty (and the range) is smaller
(b) B — the average is closer to the accepted value
(c) Take some other route (e.g. reduce heat losses), as neither of the average + uncertainty values gives the accepted result.

(19) No, since the uncertainty limits do not overlap.

(20) **(a)** It is difficult to stir inside a volumetric flask because the neck is so narrow. Heating the flask would make it expand and the graduation mark would be inaccurate.
(b) The solid may not dissolve and, anyway, the volume may change (see **(d)**).
(c) The solution will mix quickly by diffusion, so you would be sucking out solution, not just water.
(d) When a solid dissolves in a liquid, the volume of the liquid changes (it often increases, but sometimes decreases). This would make this method inaccurate.

(21) **(a)** Run $12.5\,cm^3$ from a burette into a $250\,cm^3$ volumetric flask and make up to the mark with distilled water.
(b) 0.08% in $250\,cm^3$ volumetric flask; 0.5% (± 0.0005) in 0.100; 1% (± 0.1) in burette. Total uncertainty is 2% (to 1 s.f.). Hence the uncertainty is 0.0050 ± 0.0001.

(22) new volume × new concentration = old volume × old concentration
new concentration = $10 \times 0.50/110 = 0.0045\,mol\,dm^{-3}$

(23) **(a)** The solution in the burette is slightly too dilute, so more is required and the titre is larger.
(b) The solution in the flask is slightly too dilute, so the titre is smaller.
(c) No effect (same number of moles in the flask).
(d) There are more moles in the flask, so the titre is larger.

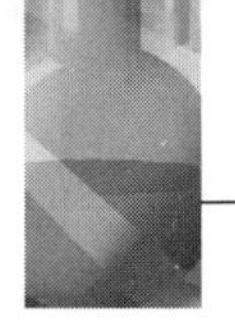

(e) There are fewer moles in the flask, so the titre is smaller.

(f) Drips fall from the funnel, increasing the volume added from the burette, so the titre appears smaller.

(g) Same as **(c)** — no effect (this is good practice).

(24)

Start/**cm³**	0.00	0.00	0.15	0.15
Finish/**cm³**	26.00	25.40	25.55	25.55
Volume/**cm³**	26.00	25.40	25.40	25.40

Changes are in bold. You may also have swapped the 'start' and 'finish' lines.

(25) (a) $C_4H_9OH + HBr \rightarrow C_4H_9Br + H_2O$

(b) M_r of C_4H_9OH = 74.0; M_r of C_4H_9Br = 136.9
maximum amount of C_4H_9Br = 5.0/74.0 mol = 5.0 × 136.9/74 = 9.25 g
% yield = 3.2 × 100/9.25 = 35%

(26) M_r of $C_6H_5NH_2$ = 93.0; M_r of $C_6H_5NO_2$ = 123.0 (mole ratio is 1:1)
12 g $C_6H_5NH_2$ = 12/93.0 = 0.129 mol
amount of $C_6H_5NO_2$ required = 0.129 × 100/40 = 0.322 mol
mass $C_6H_5NO_2$ = 0.322 × 123.0 = 40 g (2 s.f.)

(27) (a) 0.79 ± 0.05

(b) Repeat with a spot of compound Z on the base line. This should rise to the same height as compound C.

(28) (a) Remember it must be a chemistry investigation, not a physics one.

(b) This is very limited for four weeks' work. You should consider extending the investigation from what has been done in the activity.

(c) Sounds good to me, but can you fit it all in?

(d) Great — but what measurements are you going to make? Are you going to use a spectrophotometer to measure the frequency of maximum absorbance?

(e) Sounds good.

(f) Didn't we do this one in Year 9? What A2 material is there?

(g) Well, it's bound to, isn't it? Otherwise the firm would be in trouble.

(h) Sounds good.

(29) (a) These precautions are for concentrated sulfuric acid, which the student is not using.

(b) The student is not reacting magnesium with either silver nitrate or sulfur. It would be better to say that magnesium should be kept away from flames and that the hydrogen produced is explosive and should not be ignited.

(c) What sort of care? Carry out the experiment in a fume cupboard.

(d) These are standard precautions — *how* is the reagent harmful? What precautions follow from this?

(30)
- Link the references to the places in the report to which they are relevant.
- Give a longer list.
- Give the title, author, publisher, edition and page number for books.

- Give date accessed and a summary of content as well as the URL for a website.

(31) Statements **(a)** to **(e)** are investigations based on kinetics experiments, in order of gradually increasing demand. Statement **(e)** has potentially the highest demand, because the student has to work out which cations and anions to use and relate these to a pattern.

Statement **(f)** also has potentially high demand, as the student has devised his or her own experiments.

Statement **(g)** has low demand, as the aspirin content of the tablets is known already and the method is in an activity.

Statement **(h)** has potentially much higher demand as the student has devised his/her own experiments and also tested methods of determining purity.

(32)

T/K	Rate	$\frac{10^3}{T}$/K^{-1}	ln rate
278	1.5	3.60	0.41
298	41	3.36	3.7
308	200	3.25	5.3
323	1400	3.10	7.2

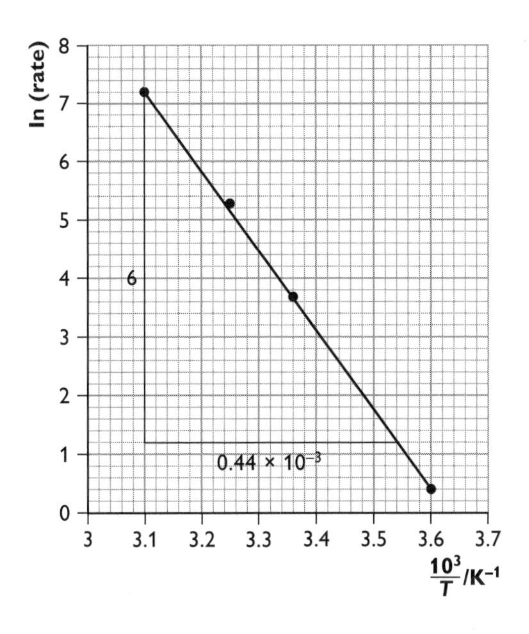

Gradient = $-E_a/R = -6/0.44 \times 10^{-3} = -13600$ (allow yourself ±200 variation around this)

So $E_a = 13600 \times 8.31 \times 10^{-3} = +110\,\text{kJ mol}^{-1}$ (2 s.f.)

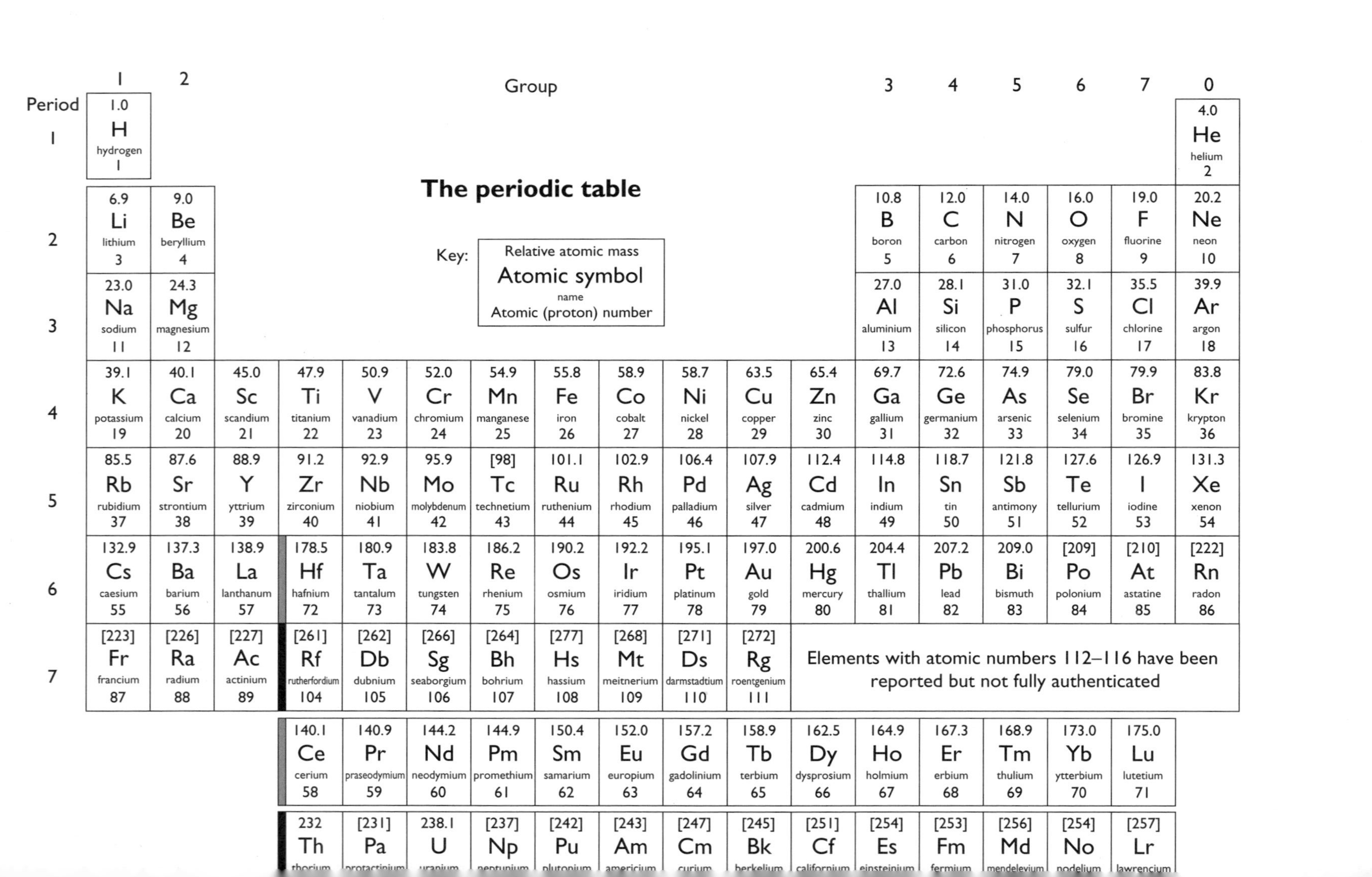

The periodic table

Key: Relative atomic mass / Atomic symbol / name / Atomic (proton) number

Period	Group 1	2											3	4	5	6	7	0
1	1.0 H hydrogen 1																	4.0 He helium 2
2	6.9 Li lithium 3	9.0 Be beryllium 4											10.8 B boron 5	12.0 C carbon 6	14.0 N nitrogen 7	16.0 O oxygen 8	19.0 F fluorine 9	20.2 Ne neon 10
3	23.0 Na sodium 11	24.3 Mg magnesium 12											27.0 Al aluminium 13	28.1 Si silicon 14	31.0 P phosphorus 15	32.1 S sulfur 16	35.5 Cl chlorine 17	39.9 Ar argon 18
4	39.1 K potassium 19	40.1 Ca calcium 20	45.0 Sc scandium 21	47.9 Ti titanium 22	50.9 V vanadium 23	52.0 Cr chromium 24	54.9 Mn manganese 25	55.8 Fe iron 26	58.9 Co cobalt 27	58.7 Ni nickel 28	63.5 Cu copper 29	65.4 Zn zinc 30	69.7 Ga gallium 31	72.6 Ge germanium 32	74.9 As arsenic 33	79.0 Se selenium 34	79.9 Br bromine 35	83.8 Kr krypton 36
5	85.5 Rb rubidium 37	87.6 Sr strontium 38	88.9 Y yttrium 39	91.2 Zr zirconium 40	92.9 Nb niobium 41	95.9 Mo molybdenum 42	[98] Tc technetium 43	101.1 Ru ruthenium 44	102.9 Rh rhodium 45	106.4 Pd palladium 46	107.9 Ag silver 47	112.4 Cd cadmium 48	114.8 In indium 49	118.7 Sn tin 50	121.8 Sb antimony 51	127.6 Te tellurium 52	126.9 I iodine 53	131.3 Xe xenon 54
6	132.9 Cs caesium 55	137.3 Ba barium 56	138.9 La lanthanum 57	178.5 Hf hafnium 72	180.9 Ta tantalum 73	183.8 W tungsten 74	186.2 Re rhenium 75	190.2 Os osmium 76	192.2 Ir iridium 77	195.1 Pt platinum 78	197.0 Au gold 79	200.6 Hg mercury 80	204.4 Tl thallium 81	207.2 Pb lead 82	209.0 Bi bismuth 83	[209] Po polonium 84	[210] At astatine 85	[222] Rn radon 86
7	[223] Fr francium 87	[226] Ra radium 88	[227] Ac actinium 89	[261] Rf rutherfordium 104	[262] Db dubnium 105	[266] Sg seaborgium 106	[264] Bh bohrium 107	[277] Hs hassium 108	[268] Mt meitnerium 109	[271] Ds darmstadtium 110	[272] Rg roentgenium 111	Elements with atomic numbers 112–116 have been reported but not fully authenticated						
				140.1 Ce cerium 58	140.9 Pr praseodymium 59	144.2 Nd neodymium 60	144.9 Pm promethium 61	150.4 Sm samarium 62	152.0 Eu europium 63	157.2 Gd gadolinium 64	158.9 Tb terbium 65	162.5 Dy dysprosium 66	164.9 Ho holmium 67	167.3 Er erbium 68	168.9 Tm thulium 69	173.0 Yb ytterbium 70	175.0 Lu lutetium 71	
				232 Th thorium	[231] Pa protactinium	238.1 U uranium	[237] Np neptunium	[242] Pu plutonium	[243] Am americium	[247] Cm curium	[245] Bk berkelium	[251] Cf californium	[254] Es einsteinium	[253] Fm fermium	[256] Md mendelevium	[254] No nobelium	[257] Lr lawrencium	